PRESERV
LOCOMO
OF BRITISH RAILWAYS

PRESERVED LOCOMOTIVES OF BRITISH RAILWAYS

SEVENTH EDITION

The Complete guide to All Remaining ex-BR and Constituent
Companies' Steam, Diesel & Electric Locomotives
and Diesel & Electric Multiple Units

Peter Fox & Neil Webster

CONTENTS

INTRODUCTION

This is the seventh edition of PRESERVED LOCOMOTIVES. The definition of 'Preserved' approp-
riate to this publication includes any ex BR or constituent companies' locomotives that still exist.
Thus all steam, diesel and electric locomotives and multiple units are shown whether 'preserved'
in the normal sense of the word or not. The locomotives are arranged generally in numerical
order of the BR number, except that very old locos which did not receive numbers in the series
pertaining at nationalisation in 1948 are listed at the end of each pre-nationalisation company
section. BR diesel locomotives are arranged in order of the "D" numbers. Notes regarding the
class details are to be found on the inside front cover of this book. Ex WD steam locomotives
are also shown, but it should be noted that as far as shunters are concerned, only those locomotives which have been preserved directly from WD stock are shown. Large numbers of such
locomotives which were in WD hands for a short period of time and then spent the rest of their
working days as industrial locomotives are not shown.

SPECIAL NOTE: Certain steam locomotives are often be found working steam specials on BR
main-line routes. These are marked in this book with a ★. It should be noted that some of these
locos can often be found at sites well away from their normal home.

The authors would be pleased to hear of any updates or amendments to the information contained herein. These should be sent to the address shown on the title page.

We would like to thank Mr. P. Hall for help in compiling this book, plus the photographers whose
photographs appear herein.

Published by Platform 5 Publishing Ltd., Lydgate House, Lydgate Lane, Sheffield S10 5FH.

ISBN 1 872524 27 3

©1991 Platform 5 Publishing Ltd.

◄Ex LMS 'Princess Royal' pacific 6201 PRINCESS ELIZABETH blasts through Bangor with the
Crewe–Chester–Holyhead 'Ynys Mon Express' of 13th October 1960   *Brian Dobbs*

GREAT WESTERN RAILWAY AND ABSORBED COMPANIES' LOCOS

GENERAL

The GWR was the only one of the big four companies which was essentially an existing company. A number of smaller companies were absorbed at the grouping. These were virtually all in Wales and included the Cambrian Railways., Cardiff Railway, Rhymney Railway and Taff Vale Railway. Prior to 1923 the GWR had also absorbed smaller concerns at various dates.

NUMBERING & CLASSIFICATION SYSTEM

The locomotives of the absorbed companies were given the lower numbers and GWR classes the higher numbers. Instead of arranging classes in blocks, the GWR adopted a strange system whereby the second digit remained constant within a class, e.g. the 0–6–2Ts numbered 5600–99 continued with 6600–99. Sometimes earlier numbers were filled in, e.g. 5101–99 continued with 4100–99. Classes were always denoted by the number of the first member of the class to be built, which was not always the lowest number in the series. GWR locos were not renumbered by BR on nationalisation.

POWER CLASS & ROUTE RESTRICTION SYSTEM

The GWR adopted a power classification letter code system which ranged from A to E in ascending order of power. Certain small locos which were below group A were said to be unclassified and the 'Kings' were classed as 'special' being higher than 'E'.

Route restriction was denoted by a system of coloured spots painted on the cabside. In ascending order of restriction these were as follows: Yellow, Blue, Red, Double Red. Where no restriction is specified, locomotives were unrestricted.

STEAM LOCOMOTIVES

CORRIS RAILWAY   0–4–2ST

Built: 1878 by Falcon Engine & Co. as 0–4–0ST.
B.P.: 160 lbf/sq. in.   **Wheel dias.:** 2' 6", 10".   **T.E.:** 2670 lbf.
Cyls.: 7" x 12" (O).   **Weight:** 9 tons.   **Gauge:** 2' 3".
Valve Gear: Stephenson.

3   "SIR HAYDN"   Talyllyn Railway   Fal 323/1878 reb. 1901

CORRIS RAILWAY   0–4–2ST

Built: 1921.
B.P.: 160 lbf/sq. in.   **Wheel dias.:** 2' 0", 1' 4½".   **T.E.:** 3330 lbf.
Cyls.: 7" x 12" (O).   **Weight:** 8 tons.   **Gauge:** 2' 3".
Valve Gear: Hackworth.

4   "EDWARD THOMAS"   Talyllyn Railway   Kerr Stuart 4047/1921

VALE OF RHEIDOL 2–6–2T

Built: 1902 by Davies & Metcalfe (9) GWR development 1923 (7, 8).
B.P.: 165 lbf/sq. in. **Wheel dias.:** 2′ 0″, 2′ 6″, 2′ 0″. **T.E.:** 10 510 lbf.
Cyls.: 11½″ x 17″ (O). **Weight:** 25 tons. **Gauge:** 1′ 11½″.
Valve Gear: Walschaerts.

BR	GWR	VOR				
7*	7		OWAIN GLYNDŴR	Vale of Rheidol Railway		Swindon 1923
8	8*		LLYWELYN	Vale of Rheidol Railway		Swindon 1923
9*	1213	2	PRINCE OF WALES	Vale of Rheidol Railway	DM 2/1902 reb.	Swindon 1923

No. 9 was under repair at the Brecon Mountain Railway at the time of writing.

No. 12 4wT

Built: 1926. Sentinel vertical-boilered geared loco. Returned to manufacturer after 3 months
service.
B.P.: 275 lbf/sq. in. **Wheel dia.:** 2′ 6″. **T.E.:** 7200 lbf.
Cyls.: 6¾″ x 9″ (I). **Weight:** 20 tons.
Valve Gear: Rotary cam.

GWR	Present		
12	49 "No. 2 ISEBROOK"	Buckinghamshire Railway Centre	S 6515/1926

OXFORD, WORCESTER & WOLVERHAMPTON RLY. 0–6–0

Built: 1855 as 0–4–0T. Sectioned exhibit. At present dismantled.
B.P.: **Wheel dia.:** **T.E.:**
Cyls.: **Weight:**

252		Leeds City Museum of Industry & Science	E.B. Wilson 1855

TAFF VALE RAILWAY CLASS O2 0–6–2T

Built: 1899 by Neilson, Reid. Sold by GWR 1926. 9 built.
B.P.: 160 lbf/sq. in. **Wheel dias.:** 4′ 6½″, 3′ 1″. **T.E.:** 19 870 lbf.
Cyls.: 17½″ x 26″ (I). **Weight:** 61.5 tons.
Valve Gear: Stephenson. **Power class:** B. **Restriction:** Blue.

GWR	TVR		
426	85	Keighley & Worth Valley Railway	NR 5408/1899

TAFF VALE RAILWAY CLASS O1 0–6–2T

Built: 1894–97. Survivor sold by GWR 1927. 14 built.
B.P.: 150 lbf/sq. in. **Wheel dias.:** 4′ 6½″, 3′ 8¾″. **T.E.:** 18 630 lbf.
Cyls.: 17½″ x 26″ (I). **Weight:** 56.4 tons.
Valve Gear: Stephenson. **Power class:** A. **Restriction:** Yellow.

GWR	TVR		
450	28*	Caerphilly Railway Soc (N)	Cardiff West Yard 306/1897

PORT TALBOT RAILWAY 0–6–0ST

Built: 1900/01. Survivor sold by GWR 1934. 6 built.
B.P.: 160 lbf/sq. in. **Wheel dia.:** 4′ 0½″. **T.E.:** 17 230 lbf.
Cyls.: 16″ x 24″ (I). **Weight:** 44 tons.
Valve Gear: Stephenson. **Power class:** A. **Restriction:** Yellow.

GWR	PTR		
813	26	Severn Valley Railway	HC555/1901

WELSHPOOL & LLANFAIR RAILWAY 0–6–0T

Built: 1903. 2 built.
B.P.: 150 lbf/sq. in. **Wheel dia.:** 2′ 9″. **T.E.:** 8180 lbf.
Cyls.: 11½″ x 16″ (O). **Weight:** 19.9 tons. **Valve Gear:** Walschaerts.

BR	GWR	W&L			
822	822	1*	THE EARL	Welshpool & Llanfair Railway	BP 3496/1903
823	823	2*	THE COUNTESS§	Welshpool & Llanfair Railway	BP 3497/1903

§ Name altered to COUNTESS by GWR. Now renamed THE COUNTESS.

POWLESLAND & MASON   0–4–0ST

Built: 1903–06. Survivor sold by GWR 1928.
B.P.: 140 lbf/sq. in.   **Wheel dia.:** 3′ 6″.   **T.E.:** 11 110 lbf.
Cyls.: 14″ x 20″ (O).   **Weight:** 24.85 tons.
Valve Gear: Stephenson.

GWR	P&M			
921*	6		The Industrial Adventure, Coalville	BE 314/1906

CARDIFF RAILWAY   0–4–0ST

Built: 1898. Rebuilt Tyndall St. Works 1916.
B.P.: 160 lbf/sq. in.   **Wheel dia.:** 3′ 2½″.   **T.E.:** 14 540 lbf.
Cyls.: 14″ x 21″ (O).   **Weight:** 25.5 tons.
Valve Gear: Kitson.

GWR	CAR.R.			
1338*	5		Didcot Railway Centre	K 3799/1898

ALEXANDRA DOCKS & RLY CO.   0–4–0ST

Built: 1897. Rebuilt Swindon, 1903. Sold by GWR 1932.
B.P.: 120 lbf/sq. in.   **Wheel dia.:** 3′ 0″.   **T.E.:** 11 110 lbf.
Cyls.: 14″ x 20″ (O).   **Weight:** 22.5 tons.
Valve Gear: Stephenson.

GWR		AD		
1340*	TROJAN	TROJAN	Didcot Railway Centre	AE 1386/1897

1361 CLASS   0–6–0ST

Built: 1910. Churchward design for dock shunting. 5 built (1361–5).
B.P.: 150 lbf/sq. in.   **Wheel dia.:** 3′ 8″.   **T.E.:** 14 840 lbf.
Cyls.: 16″ x 20″ (O).   **Weight:** 35.2 tons.
Valve Gear: Allan.

1363	Didcot Railway Centre	Swindon 2377/1910

1366 CLASS   0–6–0PT

Built: 1934. Collett design for dock shunting. Used to work Weymouth Quay boat trains. 6 built. (1366–71).
B.P.: 165 lbf/sq. in.   **Wheel dia.:** 3′ 8″.   **T.E.:** 16 320 lbf.
Cyls.: 16″ x 20″ (O).   **Weight:** 35.75 tons.
Valve Gear: Stephenson.

1369	South Devon Railway	Swindon 1934

NORTH PEMBROKESHIRE & FISHGUARD RLYS   0–6–0ST

Built: 1878. Absorbed by GWR 1898. Sold to Gwendraeth Valleys Railway in 1910. Absorbed by GWR again in 1923 but sold in March of that year.
B.P.: 140 lbf/sq. in.   **Wheel dia.:** 4′ 0″.   **T.E.:** 13 960 lbf.
Cyls.: 16″ x 22″ (I).   **Weight:** 30.95 tons.
Valve Gear: Stephenson.

GWR	GVR			
1378	2*	MARGARET	Scolton Manor Museum	Fox Walker 410/1878

1400 CLASS   0–4–2T

Built: 1932–36. Collett design. Push & Pull fitted. Locos renumbered in 1946. 75 built.(1400–74).
B.P.: 165 lbf/sq. in.   **Wheel dia.:** 5′ 2″, 3′ 8″.   **T.E.:** 13 900 lbf.
Cyls.: 16″ x 24″ (I).   **Weight:** 41.3 tons.
Valve Gear: Stephenson.   **Power Class:** Unclassified

1946 No.	1932 No.			
1420*	4820	"BULLIVER"	South Devon Railway	Swindon 1933
1442*	4842		Tiverton Museum	Swindon 1935
1450*	4850	"ASHBURTON"	South Devon Railway	Swindon 1935
1466*	4866		Didcot Railway Centre	Swindon 1936

1500 CLASS   0–6–0PT

Built: 1949. Hawksworth design. 10 built (1500–09).
B.P.: 200 lbf/sq. in.   **Wheel dia.:** 4' 7½".   **T.E.:** 22 510 lbf.
Cyls.: 17½" x 24" (O).   **Weight:** 58.2 tons.
Valve Gear: Walschaerts.   **Power class:** C.   **Restriction:** Red.
1501   Severn Valley Railway   Swindon 1949

1600 CLASS   0–6–0PT

Built: 1949–55. Hawksworth design. 70 built (1600–69).
B.P.: 165 lbf/sq. in.   **Wheel dia.:** 4' 1½".   **T.E.:** 18 510 lbf.
Cyls.: 16½" x 24" (I).   **Weight:** 41.6 tons.
Valve Gear: Stephenson.   **Power class:** A.
1638   South Devon Railway   Swindon 1951

2251 CLASS   0–6–0

Built: 1930–48 Collett design. 120 built (2251–99, 2200–50, 3200–19).
B.P.: 200 lbf/sq. in.   **Weight –Loco:** 43.4 tons.   **Wheel dia.:** 5' 2".
Cyls.: 17½" x 24" (I).   **–Tender:** 36.75 tons.   **T.E.:** 20 150 lbf.
Valve Gear: Stephenson.   **Power class:** B.   **Restriction:** Yellow.
3205   West Somerset Railway   Swindon 1946

2301 CLASS   0–6–0

Built: 1883–99. Dean design. 280 built (2301–2580).
B.P.: 180 lbf/sq. in.   **Weight –Loco:** 37 tons.   **Wheel dias.:** 5' 2".
Cyls.: 17½" x 24" (I).   **–Tender:** 36.75 tons.   **T.E.:** 18 140 lbf.
Valve Gear: Stephenson.   **Power class:** A.
2516   Great Western Railway Museum (N)   Swindon 1557/1897

2800 CLASS   2–8–0

Built: 1903–19. Churchward design for heavy freight. A later batch sometimes known as the 2884 class was built under Collett from 1938–42. These had side window cabs. 165 built (2800–99, 3800–64).
B.P.: 225 lbf/sq. in.   **Weight –Loco:** 75.5 (76.25§) tons.   **Wheel dias.:** 3' 2", 4' 7½".
Cyls.: 18½" x 30" (O).   **–Tender:** 43.15 tons.   **T.E.:** 35 380 lbf.
Valve Gear: Stephenson.   **Power class:** E.   **Restriction:** Blue.

2807	Birmingham Railway Museum	Swindon 2102/1905
2818	National Railway Museum	Swindon 2122/1905
2857	Severn Valley Railway	Swindon 2763/1918
2859	Llangollen Railway	Swindon 2765/1918
2861	Butetown Historic Railway Society	Swindon 2767/1918
2873	Birmingham Railway Museum	Swindon 2779/1918
2874	Pontypool & Blaenavon Railway	Swindon 2780/1918
2885§	Southall Railway Centre	Swindon 1938
3802§	Bodmin Steam Railway	Swindon 1938
3803§	South Devon Railway (under repair at Tyseley)	Swindon 1939
3814§	North Yorkshire Moors Railway	Swindon 1940
3822§	Didcot Railway Centre	Swindon 1940
3845§	Brighton Locomotive Works	Swindon 1942
3850§	West Somerset Railway	Swindon 1942
3855§	Pontypool & Blaenavon Railway	Swindon 1942
3862§	Northampton Steam Railway	Swindon 1942

3200 CLASS   "DUKEDOG"   4–4–0

Built: Rebuilt 1936–39 by Collett using the frames of "Bulldogs" in the boilers of "Dukes". 30 built (9000–29).
B.P.: 180 lbf/sq. in.   **Weight –Loco:** 49 tons.   **Wheel dias.:** 3' 8", 5' 8".
Cyls.: 18" x 26" (I).   **–Tender:** 40 tons.   **T.E.:** 18 950 lbf.
Valve Gear: Stephenson.   **Power class:** B.   **Restriction:** Yellow.
3217*–9017   "EARL OF BERKELEY"   Bluebell Railway   Swindon 1938

3700 CLASS   CITY   4–4–0

Built: 1903. Churchward design. Reputed to be the first loco to attain 100 mph when it hauled an "Ocean Mails" special from Plymouth to Paddington in 1904.
B.P.: 200 lbf/sq. in.   **Weight –Loco:** 55.3 tons.   **Wheel dias.:** 3' 2", 6' 8½".
Cyls.: 18" x 26" (I).   **–Tender:** 36.75 tons.   **T.E.:** 17 800 lbf.
Valve Gear: Stephenson.

BR	GWR			
3440*★	3717	CITY OF TRURO	National Railway Museum	Swindon 2000/1903

4000 CLASS   STAR   4–6–0

Built: 1906–23. Churchward design for express passenger trains. 73 built (4000–72).
B.P.: 225 lbf/sq. in.   **Weight –Loco:** 75.6 tons.   **Wheel dias.:** 3' 2", 6' 8½".
Cyls.: 15" x 26" (4).   **–Tender:** 40 tons.   **T.E.:** 27 800 lbf.
Power class: D.   **Restriction:** Red.
Valve Gear: Inside Walschaerts with rocking levers for outside valves.

4003	LODE STAR	Great Western Rly. Mus. (N)	Swindon 2231/1907

4073 CLASS   CASTLE   4–6–0

Built: 1923–50. Collett development of Star. 166 built (4073–99, 7000–37). In addition six Stars were rebuilt as Castles (111, 4000/9/16/32/7.)
B.P.: 225 lbf/sq. in.   **Weight –Loco:** 79.85 tons.   **Wheel dias.:** 3' 2", 6' 8½".
Cyls.: 16" x 26" (4).   **–Tender:** 46.7 tons.   **T.E.:** 31 630 lbf.
Power class: E.   **Restriction:** Red.
Valve Gear: Inside Walschaerts with rocking levers for outside valves.

d–Rebuilt with double chimney.

4073	CAERPHILLY CASTLE	Science Museum, London (N)	Swindon 1923
4079	PENDENNIS CASTLE	Hammersley Iron Co. Australia	Swindon 1924
5029★	NUNNEY CASTLE	Didcot Railway Centre	Swindon 1934
5043d	EARL OF MOUNT EDGCUMBE	Birmingham Railway Museum	Swindon 1936
5051	EARL BATHURST	Didcot Railway Centre	Swindon 1936
5080	DEFIANT	Birmingham Railway Museum	Swindon 1939
7027	THORNBURY CASTLE	South Devon Railway	Swindon 1949
7029d	CLUN CASTLE	Birmingham Railway Museum	Swindon 1950

5043 was named BARBURY CASTLE to 09/37.
5051 was named DRYSLLWYN CASTLE to 08/37.
5080 was named OGMORE CASTLE to 01/41.

Note: 5080 will be loaned to the Gloucestershire–Warwickshire Railway during 1991.

4200 CLASS   2–8–0T

Built: 1910–23. Churchward design. 105 built (4201–99, 4200, 5200–4).
B.P.: 200 lbf/sq. in.   **Wheel dias.:** 3' 2", 4' 7½".   **T.E.:** 31 450 lbf.
Cyls.: 18½" x 30" (O).   **Weight:** 81.6 tons.
Valve Gear: Stephenson.   **Power class:** E.   **Restriction:** Red.

4247	Cholsey & Wallingford Railway	Swindon 2637/1916
4248	Swindon Railway Engineering	Swindon 2638/1916
4253	Pontypool & Blaenavon Railway	Swindon 2643/1917
4270	Swansea Vale Railway	Swindon 2850/1919
4277	Gloucestershire–Warwickshire Railway	Swindon 2857/1920

4300 CLASS   2–6–0

Built: 1911–32. Churchward design. 342 built (4300–99 (renumbered from 8300–99 between 1944 and 1948), 6300–99, 7300–21, 7322–41 (renumbered from 9300–19 between 1956 and 1959).
B.P.: 200 lbf/sq. in.   **Weight –Loco:** 62 (63.85§) tons.   **Wheel dias.:** 3' 2", 5' 8".
Cyls.: 18½" x 30 (O).   **–Tender:** 40 tons.   **T.E.:** 25 670 lbf.
Valve Gear: Stephenson.   **Power class:** D.   **Restriction:** Blue.

8322–5322*	Didcot Railway Centre	Swindon 1917
9303*§–7325	Severn Valley Railway	Swindon 1932

4500 CLASS   2–6–2T

Built: 1906–24. Churchward design. (§Built 1927–29. Collett development with larger tanks). 175 built (4500–99, 5500–74).
B.P.: 200 lbf/sq. in. **Wheel dias.:** 3' 2", 4' 7½", 3' 2". **T.E.:** 21 250 lbf.
Cyls.: 17" x 24" (O). **Weight:** 57.9 tons (61 tons§).
Valve Gear: Stephenson. **Power class:** C. **Restriction:** Yellow.

4555	Paignton & Dartmouth Railway	Swindon 1924
4561	West Somerset Railway	Swindon 1924
4566	Severn Valley Railway	Swindon 1924
4588§	Paignton & Dartmouth Railway	Swindon 1927
5521§	Swindon Railway Engineering	Swindon 1927
5526§	Swindon Railway Engineering	Swindon 1928
5532§	Llangollen Railway	Swindon 1928
5538§	Steamtown Carnforth	Swindon 1928
5539§	Butetown Historic Railway Society	Swindon 1928
5541§	Dean Forest Railway	Swindon 1928
5542§	West Somerset Railway	Swindon 1928
5552§	Bodmin Steam Railway	Swindon 1928
5553§	Dean Forest Railway	Swindon 1928
5572§	Didcot Railway Centre	Swindon 1929

Notes: 4566 will be loaned to the South Devon Railway for the summer of 1991. 5542 is under restoration on a site in Taunton.

4900 CLASS   HALL   4–6–0

Built: 1928–43. Collett development of Churchward 'Saint' class (4900 rebuilt from Saint). 259 built (4900–99, 5900–99, 6900–58).
B.P.: 225 lbf/sq. in. **Weight –Loco:** 75 tons. **Wheel dias.:** 3' 2", 6' 0".
Cyls.: 18½" x 30" (O). **–Tender:** 46.7 tons. **T.E.:** 27 270 lbf.
Valve Gear: Stephenson. **Power class:** D. **Restriction:** Red.

4920	DUMBLETON HALL	South Devon Railway	Swindon 1929
4930	HAGLEY HALL	Severn Valley Railway	Swindon 1929
4936	KINLET HALL	Gloucestershire–Warwickshire Railway	Swindon 1929
4942	MAINDY HALL	Didcot Railway Centre	Swindon 1929
4953	PITCHFORD HALL	Dean Forest Railway	Swindon 1929
4979	WOOTTON HALL	Fleetwood Locomotive Centre	Swindon 1930
4983	ALBERT HALL	Birmingham Railway Museum	Swindon 1931
5900	HINDERTON HALL	Didcot Railway Centre	Swindon 1931
5952	COGAN HALL	Llangollen Railway	Swindon 1935
5967	BICKMARSH HALL	Pontypool & Blaenavon Railway	Swindon 1937
5972	OLTON HALL	Bombardier Prorail, Wakefield	Swindon 1937

5101 CLASS   2–6–2T

Built: 1929–49. Collett development of Churchward 3100 class. 180 built (5101–99, 4100–79).
B.P.: 200 lbf/sq. in. **Wheel dias.:** 3' 2", 5' 8", 3' 8". **T.E.:** 24 300 lbf.
Cyls.: 18" x 30" (O). **Weight:** 78.45 tons.
Valve Gear: Stephenson. **Power class:** D. **Restriction:** Yellow.

4110	Southall Railway Centre	Swindon 1936
4115	Butetown Historic Railway Society	Swindon 1936
4121	Swindon Railway Engineering	Swindon 1937
4141	Swindon Railway Engineering	Swindon 1946
4144	Didcot Railway Centre	Swindon 1946
4150	Severn Valley Railway	Swindon 1947
4160	West Somerset Railway	Swindon 1948
5164	Severn Valley Railway	Swindon 1930
5193	Steamport Railway Museum	Swindon 1934
5199	Long Marston (ex MoD)	Swindon 1934

5205 CLASS   2–8–0T

Built: 1923–25/40. Collett development of 4200 class. 60 built (5205–64).
B.P.: 200 lbf/sq. in. **Wheel dias.:** 3' 2", 4' 7½". **T.E.:** 33 170 lbf.
Cyls.: 19" x 30" (O). **Weight:** 82.1 tons.
Valve Gear: Stephenson. **Power class:** E. **Restriction:** Red.

5224		Great Central Railway	Swindon 1925
5227		Butetown Historic Railway Society	Swindon 1924
5239	"GOLIATH"	South Devon Railway	Swindon 1924

5600 CLASS 0–6–2T

Built: 1924–28. Collett design. 200 built (5600–99, 6600–99).
B.P.: 200 lbf/sq. in. **Wheel dias.:** 4' 7½", 3' 8". **T.E.:** 25 800 lbf.
Cyls.: 18" x 26" (I). **Weight:** 68 tons.
Valve Gear: Stephenson. **Power class:** D. **Restriction:** Red.

5619	Telford Steam Railway	Swindon 1925
5637	Swindon & Cricklade Railway	Swindon 1925
5643	Lakeside & Haverthwaite Railway	Swindon 1925
5668	Pontypool & Blaenavon Railway	Swindon 1926
6619	North Yorkshire Moors Railway	Swindon 1928
6634	East Somerset Railway	Swindon 1928
6686	Butetown Historic Railway Society	AW 974/1928
6695	Swanage Railway	AW 983/1928
6697	Didcot Railway Centre	AW 985/1928

5700 CLASS 0–6–0PT

Built: 1929–49. Collett design. The standard GWR shunter. 863 built (5700–99, 6700–79, 7700–99, 8701–99, 8700–99, 3700–99, 3600–99, 4600–99, 9600–82,
B.P.: 200 lbf/sq. in. **Wheel dias.:** 4' 7½" **T.E.:** 22 510 lbf.
Cyls.: 17½" x 24" (I). **Weight:** 47.5 (49§) tons.
Power Class: C.
Valve Gear: Stephenson. **Restriction:** Blue (Yellow from 1950).

GWR	LTE		
3650		Didcot Railway Centre	Swindon 1939
3738		Didcot Railway Centre	Swindon 1937
4612		Swindon Railway Engineering	Swindon 1942
5764*	L95	Severn Valley Railway	Swindon 1929
5775*	L89	Keighley & Worth Valley Railway	Swindon 1929
5786*	L92	Bulmers Railway Centre	Swindon 1930
7714		Severn Valley Railway	KS 4449/1930
7715*	L99	Buckinghamshire Railway Centre	KS 4450/1930
7752*	L94	Gloucestershire–Warwickshire Railway	NBL 24040/1930
7754		Llangollen Railway	NBL 24042/1930
7760*	L90	Birmingham Railway Museum	NBL 24048/1930
9600§		Birmingham Railway Museum	Swindon 1945
9629§		Cardiff Holiday Inn	Swindon 1946
9642§		Swansea Vale Railway	Swindon 1946
9681§		Dean Forest Railway	Swindon 1949
9682§		Southall Railway Centre	Swindon 1949

Notes: 7752 is on hire from the Birmingham Railway Museum. 7760 is on loan to the Great Central Railway for 1991.

6000 CLASS KING 4–6–0

Built: 1927–30. Collett design. 31 built.
B.P.: 250 lbf/sq. in. **Weight –Loco:** 89 tons. **Wheel dias.:** 3' 0", 6' 6".
Cyls.: 16¼" x 28" (4). **–Tender:** 46.7 tons. **T.E.:** 40 290 lbf.
Power class: Special. **Restriction:** Double Red.
Valve Gear: Inside Walschaerts with rocking levers for outside valves.

6000	KING GEORGE V	Swindon Railway Engineering (N)	Swindon 1927
6023	KING EDWARD II	Didcot Railway Centre	Swindon 1930
6024★	KING EDWARD I	Didcot Railway Centre	Swindon 1930

6100 CLASS 2–6–2T

Built: 1931–35. Collett development of 5100. 70 built (6100–69).
B.P.: 225 lbf/sq. in. **Wheel dias.:** 3' 2", 5' 8", 3' 8". **T.E.:** 27 340 lbf.
Cyls.: 18" x 30" (O). **Weight:** 78.45 tons.
Valve Gear: Stephenson. **Power class:** D. **Restriction:** Blue.

| 6106 | Didcot Railway Centre | Swindon 1931 |

(on loan to the West Somerset Railway for the remainder of 1991.)

6400 CLASS
0–6–0PT

Built: 1932–37. Collett design. Push & Pull fitted. 40 built (6400–39).
B.P.: 165 lbf/sq. in.   **Wheel dia.:** 4′ 7½″.   **T.E.:** 16 510 lbf.
Cyls.: 16½″ x 24″ (I).   **Weight:** 45.6 tons.
Valve Gear: Stephenson.   **Power class:** A.   **Restriction:** Yellow.

6412	West Somerset Railway	Swindon 1934
6430	Long Marston (ex MoD)	Swindon 1937
6435	Paignton & Dartmouth Railway	Swindon 1937

6959 CLASS   MODIFIED HALL
4–6–0

Built: 1944–49. Hawksworth development of 'Hall'. 71 built (6959–99, 7900–29).
B.P.: 225 lbf/sq. in.   **Weight –Loco:** 75.8 tons.   **Wheel dias.:** 3′ 2″, 6′ 0″.
Cyls.: 18½″ x 30″ (O).   **–Tender:** 47.3 tons.   **T.E.:** 27 270 lbf.
Valve Gear: Stephenson.   **Power class:** D.   **Restriction:** Blue.

6960	RAVENINGHAM HALL	Severn Valley Railway	Swindon 1944
6984	OWSDEN HALL	Herring Brothers, Bicester	Swindon 1948
6989	WIGHTWICK HALL	Buckinghamshire Railway Centre	Swindon 1948
6990	WITHERSLACK HALL	Great Central Railway	Swindon 1948
6998★	BURTON AGNES HALL	Didcot Railway Centre	Swindon 1949
7903	FOREMARKE HALL	Swindon & Cricklade Railway	Swindon 1949
7927	WILLINGTON HALL	Butetown Historic Railway Society	Swindon 1950

7200 CLASS
2–8–2T

Built: 1934–50. Collett rebuilds of 4200 and 5205 class 2–8–0Ts. 54 built (7200–53).
B.P.: 200 lbf/sq. in.   **Wheel dias.:** 3′ 2″, 4′ 7½″, 3′ 8″.   **T.E.:** 33 170 lbf.
Cyls.: 19″ x 30″ (O).   **Weight:** 92.6 tons.
Valve Gear: Stephenson.   **Power class:** E.   **Restriction:** Blue.

7200	(rebuilt from 5277)	Buckinghamshire Railway Centre	Swindon 1930 reb. 1934
7202	(rebuilt from 5275)	Didcot Railway Centre	Swindon 1930 reb. 1934
7229	(rebuilt from 5264)	East Lancashire Railway	Swindon 1926 reb. 1935

7800 CLASS   MANOR
4–6–0

Built: 1938–50. Collett design for secondary main lines. 30 built (7800–29).
B.P.: 225 lbf/sq. in.   **Weight –Loco:** 68.9 tons.   **Wheel dias.:** 3′ 0″, 5′ 8″.
Cyls.: 18″ x 30″ (O).   **–Tender:** 40 tons.   **T.E.:** 27 340 lbf.
Valve Gear: Stephenson.   **Power class:** D.   **Restriction:** Blue.

7802	BRADLEY MANOR	Severn Valley Railway	Swindon 1938
7808	COOKHAM MANOR	Didcot Railway Centre	Swindon 1938
7812	ERLESTOKE MANOR	Severn Valley Railway	Swindon 1939
7819★	HINTON MANOR	Severn Valley Railway	Swindon 1939
7820	DINMORE MANOR	West Somerset Railway	Swindon 1950
7821	DITCHEAT MANOR	Llangollen Railway	Swindon 1950
7822	FOXCOTE MANOR	Llangollen Railway	Swindon 1950
7827	LYDHAM MANOR	Paignton & Dartmouth Railway	Swindon 1950
7828	ODNEY MANOR	East Lancashire Railway	Swindon 1950

7812 is under restoration at Swindon Railway Engineering.
7820 is under restoration at Birmingham Railway Museum.
7828 is on loan from the Llangollen Railway.

9400 CLASS
0–6–0PT

Built: 1947–56. Hawksworth design. 210 built (9400–99, 8400–99, 3400–09).
B.P.: 200 lbf/sq. in.   **Wheel dia.:** 4′ 7½″.   **T.E.:** 22 510 lbf.
Cyls.: 17½″ x 24″ (I).   **Weight:** 55.35 tons.
Valve Gear: Stephenson.   **Power class:** C.   **Restriction:** Red.

9400	Great Western Railway Museum (N)	Swindon 1947
9466	Buckinghamshire Railway Centre	RSH 7617/1952

SHROPSHIRE & MONTGOMERY RAILWAY
0–4–2WT

Built: 1893 by Dodman. Rebuilt from 2–2–2WT.
B.P.: ? lbf/sq. in.   **Wheel dias.:** 2′ 0″,?.   **T.E.:** lbf.
Cyls.: 4″ x 9″ (I).   **Weight:** 5.5 tons.

Note: This loco together with three others (LNWR coal engines) became BR (WR) stock in 1950 when this line was nationalised. The locos were then withdrawn.

| 1 | GAZELLE | Museum of Army Transport, Beverley | Dodman 1893 |

BURRY PORT & GWENDRAETH VALLEY RAILWAY   0–6–0ST

Built: 1900.
B.P.: | **Wheel dias.:** | **T.E.:**
Cyls.: (O) | **Weight:**
Note: This loco was supplied new to the BPGVR and was sold into industrial service in 1914.

| 2 | PONTYBEREM | Didcot Railway Centre | AE 1421/1900 |

SANDY & POTTON RAILWAY   0–4–0WT

Built: 1857. The Sandy & Potton Railway became part of the LNWR and the loco worked on the Cromford & High Peak Railway from 1863–1878. The loco was sold to the Wantage Tramway in 1878.
B.P.: | **Wheel dias.:** | **T.E.:**
Cyls.: | **Weight:**

SPR	LNWR	WT		
SHANNON	1863	5	Didcot Railway Centre (N)	George England & Co. 1857

SOUTH DEVON RAILWAY   0–4–0WT

Built: 18 . Vertical boiler.
B.P.: ? lbf/sq. in. | **Wheel dias.:** 3' 0" | **T.E.:** lbf.
Cyls.: 9" x 12" (V). | **Weight:** 0 tons. | **Gauge:** 7' 0¼".

GWR	SDR		
2180	151 TINY*	South Devon Railway (N)	Sara 1868

DIESEL RAILCARS

UNCLASSIFIED   PARK ROYAL

Built: 1934 by Park Royal. Single unit.
Engines: Two AEC 90 kW (121 hp).
Body: 19.58 x 2.70 m. | **Weight:** 26.2 tons. | **Seats:** 44S.

BR	GWR		
W 4 W	4	Great Western Railway Museum (N)	PR 1934

UNCLASSIFIED   GWR

Built: 1940. Single unit.
Engines: Two AEC 78 kW (105 hp).
Body: 20.21 x 2.70 m. | **Weight:** 35.6 tons. | **Seats:** 48S.

BR	GWR		
W 20 W*	20	Kent & East Sussex Railway	Swindon 1940
W 22 W*	22	Didcot Railway Centre	Swindon 1941

SOUTHERN

SOUTHERN RAILWAY AND CONSTITUENT COMPANIES' LOCOS

GENERAL

The Southern Railway (SR) was an amalgamation of the London, Brighton and South Coast Railway (LBSCR), the London and South Western Railway (LSWR) and the South Eastern and Chatham Railway (SECR). The latter was formed in 1898 by the amalgamation of the South Eastern Railway (SER) and London, Chatham and Dover Railway (LCDR).

LOCOMOTIVE NUMBERING SYSTEM

On formation of the SR in 1924, all locomotives (including new builds) were given a prefix letter to denote the works which maintained them as follows:
A   – Ashford Works. All former SECR locos plus some D1, L1, U1.
B   – Brighton Works. All former LBSCR locos plus some D1.
E   – Eastleigh Works. All former LSWR locos plus LN, V, Z.

In 1931 locos were renumbered. 'E' prefix locos merely lost the prefix (except locos with an '0' in front of the number to which 3000 was added). 'A' prefix locos had 1000 added and 'B' prefix locos had 2000 added, e.g. B 636 became 2636, E 0298 became 3298.

In 1941 Bulleid developed a most curious numbering system for his new locos. This consisted of two numbers representing the numbers of leading and trailing axles respectively followed by a letter denoting the number of the driving axles. This was followed by the loco serial number. The first pacific was therefore 21C1, and the first Q1 0–6–0 was C1.

In 1948 British Railways added 30000 to all numbers, but the 3xxx series (formerly 0xxx series) were totally renumbered. The Q1s became 33xxx, the MNs 35xxx and the WCs 34xxx.

Isle of Wight locos had their own number series, denoted by a 'W' prefix. This indicated Ryde Works maintenance and was carried until the end of steam.

In the section which follows, locos are listed generally in order of BR numbers. Three old locos which were withdrawn before nationalisation are listed at the end of the section.

STEAM LOCOMOTIVES

CLASSIFICATION

The LBSCR originally classified loco classes by a letter which denoted the use of the class. A further development was to add a number, to identify different classes of similar use. A rebuild was signified by an 'X' suffix. In its latter years, new classes of different wheel arrangement were given different letters. The SECR gave each class a letter. A number after the letter signified either a new class which was a modification of the original or a rebuild. The SR perpetuated this system. The LSWR had an odd system based on the works order number for the first loco of the class to be built. These went A1, B1......Z1, A2......Z2, A3......etc. and did not only apply to locos. Locos bought from outside contractors were classified by the first number to be delivered, e.g. "0298 class".

CLASS O2   0–4–4T

Built: 1889–1   . Adams LSWR design.
B.P.: 160 lbf/sq. in.   **Wheel dias.:** 4' 10"   **T.E.:** 17 235 lbf.
Cyls.: 17" x 24" (I).   **Weight:** 48.4 tons.
Valve Gear: Stephenson.

Air braked.

BR	SR	LSWR			
W 24	E 209–W 24	209 CALBOURNE	Isle of Wight Steam Railway	Nine Elms 341/1891

CLASS M7   0–4–4T

Built: 1897–1911. Drummond LSWR design. 105 built.
B.P.: 175 lbf/sq. in.   **Wheel dias.:** 5' 7", 3' 7".   **T.E.:** 19 760 lbf.
Cyls.: 18½" x 26" (I).   **Weight:** 60.15 tons.
Valve Gear: Stephenson.
30053 was push and pull fitted and air braked.

BR	SR	LSWR		
30053*	E 53–53	53	Swanage Railway	Nine Elms 1905
30245	E 245–245	245*	National Railway Museum (N)	Nine Elms 501/1897

30053 is on repair at the East Anglian Railway Museum.

CLASS USA   0–6–0T

Built: 1942–3 by Vulcan Works, Wilkes–Barre, PA, USA for US Army Transportation Corps. Purche.
B.P.: 210 lbf/sq. in.   **Wheel dia.:** 4' 6"   **T.E.:** 21 600 lbf.
Cyls.: 16½" x 24" (O).   **Weight:** 46.5 tons.
Valve Gear: Walschaerts.

BR	SR	1963	Present		
30064*	64			Bluebell Railway	VIW 4432/1943
30065	65		22 MAUNSELL	Kent & East Sussex Railway	VIW 4441/1943
30070	70	DS 238	21 WAINWRIGHT	Kent & East Sussex Railway	VIW 4433/1943
30072*	72			Keighley & Worth Valley Railway	VIW 4446/1943

JZ 62.669 was built in Jugoslavia to the same design and will be restored as "30075". it is at the Swanage Railway.

CLASS B4   0–4–0T

Built: 1891–1909. Adams LSWR design for dock shunting (25 built).
B.P.: 140.lbf/sq. in.   **Wheel dia.:** 3' 9¾"   **T.E.:** 14 650 lbf.
Cyls.: 16" x 22" (O).   **Weight:** 33.45 tons.
Valve Gear: Stephenson.

BR	SR			
30096	E 96 –96*	NORMANDY	Bluebell Railway	Nine Elms 396/1893
30102	E 102–102*	GRANVILLE	Bressingham Gardens	Nine Elms 406/1893

CLASS T9   4–4–0

Built: 1889–1924. Drummond LSWR express passenger design. 66 built.
B.P.: 175 lbf/sq. in.   **Weight –Loco:** 51.8 tons.   **Wheel dias.:** 3' 7", 6' 7".
Cyls.: 19" x 26" (I).   **–Tender:** 44.85 tons.   **T.E.:** 17 670 lbf.
Valve Gear: Stephenson.

BR	SR	LSWR		
30120	E 120–120*	120	Swanage Railway (N)	Nine Elms 572/1899

CLASS S15   (URIE)   4–6–0

Built: 1920–1921. Urie LSWR design. 20 built.
B.P.: 180 lbf/sq. in.   **Weight –Loco:** 79.8 tons.   **Wheel dias.:** 3' 7", 5' 7".
Cyls.: 21" x 28" (O).   **–Tender:** 57.8 tons.   **T.E.:** 28 200 lbf.
Valve Gear: Walschaerts.

BR	SR	LSWR		
30499*	E499–499	499	Watercress Line	Eastleigh 1920
30506	E506–506	506*	Watercress Line	Eastleigh 1920

CLASS Q   0–6–0

Built: 1938–39. Maunsell SR design. 20 built (30530–49).
B.P.: 200 lbf/sq. in.   **Weight –Loco:** 49.5 tons.   **Wheel dias.:** 5' 1".
Cyls.: 19" x 26" (I).   **–Tender:** 40.5 tons.   **T.E.:** 26 160 lbf.
Valve Gear: Stephenson.

BR	SR			
30541	541*		Bluebell Railway	Eastleigh 1939

0415 CLASS 4-4-2T

Built: 1882–85. Adams LSWR design. 72 built.
B.P.: 160 lbf/sq. in.   **Wheel dias.**: 3' 0", 5' 7", 3' 0"   **T.E.**: 14 920 lbf.
Cyls.: 17½" x 24" (O).   **Weight**: 55.25 tons.
Valve Gear: Stephenson.

BR	SR	LSWR		
30583	E 0488–3488	488*	Bluebell Railway	N 3209/1885

0298 CLASS 2-4-0WT

Built: 1863–75. W. G. Beattie LSWR design. Last used on the Wenford Bridge branch in Cornwall. 85 built. Survivors reboilered in 1921.
B.P.: 160 lbf/sq. in.   **Wheel dias.**: 3' 7¾", 5' 7".   **T.E.**: 12 160 lbf.
Cyls.: 16½" x 22" (O).   **Weight**: 35.75 (36.3§) tons.
Valve Gear: Allan.

BR	SR	LSWR		
30585§	E 0314–3314	0314*	Bucks. Rly. Centre	BP 1414/1874 reb Elh 1921
30587*	E 0298–3298	0298	South Devon Railway (N)	BP 1412/1874 reb Elh 1921

CLASS N15 KING ARTHUR 4-6-0

Built: 1925–27. Maunsell SR development of Urie LSWR design. 54 built (30448–457, 30763–806).
B.P.: 200 lbf/sq. in.   **Weight –Loco**: 80.7 tons.   **Wheel dias.**: 3' 7", 6' 7".
Cyls.: 20½" x 28" (O).   **–Tender**: 56.4 tons.   **T.E.**: 25 320 lbf.
Valve Gear: Walschaerts.

BR	SR			
30777	777*★	SIR LAMIEL	Humberside LPG (N)	NBL 23223/1925

CLASS S15 (MAUNSELL) 4-6-0

Built: 1927–36. Maunsell SR development of Urie LSWR design.
B.P.: 200 lbf/sq. in.   **Weight –Loco**: 80.7 (79.25§) tons.   **Wheel dias.**: 3' 7", 5' 7".
Cyls.: 20½" x 28" (O).   **–Tender**: 56.4 tons.   **T.E.**: 29 860 lbf.
Valve Gear: Walschaerts.

† Frames only remain.

BR	SR		
30825*	825	North Yorkshire Moors Railway†	Eastleigh 1927
30828*	828	BRML Eastleigh Works	Eastleigh 1927
30830*	830	Bluebell Railway	Eastleigh 1927
30841§	841*	North Yorkshire Moors Railway	Eastleigh 1936
30847§*	847	Bluebell Railway	Eastleigh 1936

CLASS LN LORD NELSON 4-6-0

Built: 1926–29. Maunsell SR design. 16 built (30850–65).
B.P.: 220 lbf/sq. in.   **Weight –Loco**: 83.5 tons.   **Wheel dias.**: 3' 1", 6' 7".
Cyls.: 16½" x 26" (4).   **–Tender**: 56.7 tons.   **T.E.**: 33 510 lbf.
Valve Gear: Walschaerts.

BR	SR			
30850	E850–850*★	LORD NELSON	Steamtown Carnforth (N)	Eastleigh 1926

CLASS V SCHOOLS 4-4-0

Built: 1930–35. Maunsell SR design. 40 built (30900–39).
B.P.: 220 lbf/sq. in.   **Weight –Loco**: 67.1 tons.   **Wheel dias.**: 3' 1", 6' 7".
Cyls.: 16½" x 26" (3).   **–Tender**: 42.4 tons.   **T.E.**: 25 130 lbf.
Valve Gear: Walschaerts.

BR	SR			
30925*	925	CHELTENHAM	National Railway Museum	Eastleigh 1934
30926*	926	REPTON	North Yorkshire Moors Railway	Eastleigh 1934
30928	928*	STOWE	Bluebell Railway	Eastleigh 1934

CLASS P   0–6–0T

Built: 1909–10. Wainwright SECR design. 8 built.
B.P.: 160 lbf/sq. in.   **Wheel dias.:** 3′ 9″.   **T.E.:** 7830 lbf.
Cyls.: 12″ x 18″ (I).   **Weight:** 28.5 tons.
Valve Gear: Stephenson.
§ Push & pull fitted.

BR	SR	SECR		
31027	A 27–1027	27*	Bluebell Railway	Ashford 1910
31178	A 178–1178*	178	Bluebell Railway	Ashford 1910
31323*	A 323–1323	323	Bluebell Railway	Ashford 1910
31556	A 556–1556*	753	Kent & East Sussex Railway	Ashford 1909

CLASS O1   0–6–0

Built: 1903–15. Wainwright SECR design. 66 built. 59 were rebuilt out of 122 "O" class.
B.P.: 150 lbf/sq. in.   **Weight –Loco:** 41.05 tons.   **Wheel dia.:** 5′ 1″.
Cyls.: 18″ x 26″ (I).   **–Tender:** 25.45 tons.   **T.E.:** 17 610 lbf.
Valve Gear: Stephenson.

BR	SR	SECR		
31065	A 65–1065	65*	A.J. Birch, Hope Farm, Sellindge	Ashford 1896 reb. 1908

Note: Only the boiler & cab are at Sellindge. The location of the rest of this loco. is unknown.

CLASS H   0–4–4T

Built: 1904–15. Wainwright SECR design. 66 built.
B.P.: 160 lbf/sq. in.   **Wheel dias.:** 5′ 6″, 3′ 7″.   **T.E.:** 17 360 lbf.
Cyls.: 18″ x 26″ (I).   **Weight:** 54.4 tons.
Valve Gear: Stephenson.
Push and Pull fitted. Air brakes.

BR	SR	SECR		
31263	A 263–1263	263*	Bluebell Railway	Ashford 1905

CLASS C   0–6–0

Built: 1900–08. Wainwright SECR design. 109 built.
B.P.: 160 lbf/sq. in.   **Weight –Loco:** 43.8 tons.   **Wheel dia.:** 5′ 2″.
Cyls.: 18½″ x 26″ (I).   **–Tender:** 38.25 tons.   **T.E.:** 19 520 lbf.
Valve Gear: Stephenson.

BR	SR	SECR		
31592–DS 239	A 592–1592	592*	Bluebell Railway	Longhedge 1902

CLASS U   2–6–0

Built: 1928–31. Maunsell SR design. 50 built (31610–39, 31790–809). 31790–809 were converted from class K 2–6–4T.
B.P.: 200 lbf/sq. in.   **Weight –Loco:** 61.9 (62.55§) tons.   **Wheel dias.:** 3′ 1″, 6′ 0″.
Cyls.: 19″ x 28″ (O).   **–Tender:** 42.4 tons.   **T.E.:** 23 870 lbf.
Valve Gear: Walschaerts.
§ Formerly class K 2–6–4T A 806 RIVER TORRIDGE built Ashford 1926.

BR	SR		
31618	A 618–1618*	Bluebell Railway	Brighton 1928
31625*	A 625–1625	Watercress Line	Ashford 1929
31638*	A 638–1638	Bluebell Railway	Ashford 1931
31806*	A 806–1806§	Watercress Line	Brighton 1928

§ Formerly class K 2–6–4T A 806 RIVER TORRIDGE built Ashford 1926.

CLASS D   4–4–0

Built: 1901–7. Wainwright SECR design. 51 built.
B.P.: 175 lbf/sq. in.   **Weight –Loco:** 50 tons.   **Wheel dias.:** 3′ 7″, 6′ 8″.
Cyls.: 19¼″ x 26″ (I).   **–Tender:** 39.1 tons.   **T.E.:** 17 910 lbf.
Valve Gear: Stephenson.

▲On a visit to the Gloucestershire–Warwickshire Railway, ex-GWR 4–4–0 No. 3440 CITY OF TRURO nears Hailes Abbey with the 13.15 Toddington–Gretton. This locomotive was reputed to be the first to attain 100 m.p.h. *Hugh Ballantyne*

▼GWR 'Castle' Class 4–6–0 No. 5080 DEFIANT nears Danzey with the 'Shakespeare Limited' from Tyseley to Stratford-on-Avon on 15th April 1990. *David Marriott*

GWR 5205 Class 2—8—0T 5224 approaches Quorn on the Great Central Railway with an afternoon train from Loughborough to Rothley on 5th August 1990.
David Marriott

▲'Modified Hall' 4–6–0 No. 6960 RAVENINGHAM HALL at Bewdley North on the Severn Valley Railway on 2nd December 1990 with the 10.50 Arley–Kidderminster. *Tom Clift*

▼At the end of its day's work, the Dean Forest Railway's immaculate GWR 5700 Class 0–6–0PT No. 9681 goes on shed at Norchard on 27th June 1990. *Hugh Ballantyne*

A more famous example of the 5700 Class is No. 5775 of the Keighley and Worth Valley Railway which was used in the film 'The Railway Children'. This has now been repainted in the livery used in the film and is seen approaching Oxenhope with the 15.04 from Keighley on 31st March 1990.
Doug Birmingham

▲ 'King' Class 4–6–0 No. 6024 KING EDWARD I near Henley-in-Arden with the 'Shakespeare Limited' on 16th April 1990. *David Marriott*

▼ GWR 6100 Class 2–6–2T No. 6106 near Winchcombe on the Gloucestershire–Warwickshire Railway on 14th July 1990 with the 17.00 ex-Toddington. *Bryan Hicks*

▲LSWR Class 02 0–4–4T No. 24 CALBOURNE backs off the train to run round at Havenstreet on the Isle of Wight Steam Railway, having provided steam power for the trains of the day on 17th August 1989. *Mervyn Turvey*

▼SR Class U 2–6–0 No. 1618 north of Freshfield on the Bluebell Railway with the 15.57 Sheffield Park to Horsted Keynes on 28th May 1989. *Hugh Ballantyne*

Rebuilt 'Merchant Navy' 4–6–2 No. 35028 CLAN LINE leaves Derby for Didcot with the return 'Risborough Venturer' rail tour on 28th April 1990.
David Marriott

▲On the Kent and East Sussex Railway, the 13.02 Northiam–Tenterden receives its loco., USA tank No. 30065. These locomotives came from the US Army Transportation Corps during the war.

Allan Mott

▼LSWR Urie S15 4–6–0 No. 506 passes Medstead on the Watercress Line on 2nd April 1989 with a working from Alresford to Alton.

Les Nixon

▲SR 'King Arthur' Class 4–6–0 No. 777 SIR LAMIEL approaches Rise Hill Tunnel on the Settle Jn.–Carlisle route with a return 'Cumbrian Mountain Express' on 26th May 1990. *Mike Goodfield*

▼Rebuilt 'West Country' Class 4–6–2 No. 34027 TAW VALLEY is seen leaving Llandudno with the 'North Wales Coast Express' on 19th July 1989. *Les Nixon*

▲Unrebuilt 'Battle of Britain' Class 4–6–2 No. 34072 257 SQUADRON is seen at Dover Priory after the Battle of Britain celebrations on 8th September 1990. *Chris Milner*

▼The diminutive LBSCR Class A1X 'Terrier' 0–6–0T No. 10 SUTTON (BR 32650) which belongs to the Kent and East Sussex Railway is seen working a Shuttle train service at the new station at Tyseley Warwick Road on 15th October 1989. *Hugh Ballantyne*

▲With the demise of the Dinting Railway Centre, the stock of the Bahamas Locomotive Society has now moved to the Keighley and Worth Valley Railway. Ex-LMS 'Jubilee' Class 4–6–0 No. 45596 BAHAMAS is seen here at Oxenhope on 31st March 1990, when it was a visitor for an enthusiasts' weekend. *E.H. Sawford*

▼A previous move away from Dinting was that of Rebuilt Royal Scot 4–6–0 No. 46115 SCOTS GUARDSMAN, seen at its new home at the Birmingham Railway Museum, Tyseley on 15th October 1989. The loco is in LMS lined black livery and sports its LMS number 6115, a number it never carried in rebuilt condition. *Hugh Ballantyne*

▲LMS "Black 5" 4–6–0 No. 5025 arrives at Aviemore (Speyside Railway) from Boat of Garten on 21st July 1990. *Peter Moody*

▼Ex-LMS 'Coronation' Class 4–6–2 No. 46229 DUCHESS OF HAMILTON approaches Keighley with a return 'Cumbrian Mountain Express' on 28th July 1990. *David Marriott*

Ex-LMS 'Princess Royal' Class 4–6–2 No. 46203 PRINCESS MARGARET ROSE approaches Clay Cross on 15th September 1990 with a return 'White Rose' which it worked from Sheffield to Derby.

Hugh Ballantyne

▲Ivatt Class 2MT 2–6–0 No. 46441 (carrying incorrect number "6441") at BREL Ltd's Crewe Works open day on 21st July 1990.   *Peter Rayner*

▼Ex-LMS "Jinty" 0–6–0T No. 47383 blows off vigorously as it emerges from Bewdley Tunnel with the 13.34 Kidderminster–Bridgnorth on 24th September 1989.   *Hugh Ballantyne*

▲Recently repatriated from Turkey, LMS-design Class 8F TCDD No. 45160 is seen preparing for a run with a freight train at the Swanage steam gala weekend on 17th September 1990. This was the locomotive's first run after arriving at Swanage.   *Mervyn Turvey*

▼LNWR outside-framed 2–4–0 No. 3020 CORNWALL at BREL Ltd's Crewe Works open day on 21st July 1990.   *Peter Rayner*

▲Now also on the Keighley and Worth Valley Railway ex-Dinting is LNWR 'Coal Tank' No. 1054, part of the National Collection.   *David Rodgers*

▼Another National Collection loco is Midland Railway Kirtley-designed 2–4–0 No. 158A, seen on display at Swanwick, Midland Railway Centre.   *Hugh Ballantyne*

BR	SR	SECR		
31737	A 737–1737	737*	National Railway Museum	Ashford 1901

CLASS N   2–6–0

Built: 1917–34. Maunsell SECR design. Some built by SR. 80 built.
B.P.: 200 lbf/sq. in.　　**Weight –Loco:** 59.4 tons.　　**Wheel dias.:** 3′ 1″, 5′ 6″.
Cyls.: 19″ x 28″ (O).　　　**–Tender:** 39.25 tons.　　**T.E.:** 26 040 lbf.
Valve Gear: Walschaerts.

BR	SR		
31874*	A874–1874	"BRIAN FISK"	Watercress Line	Woolwich Arsenal 1925

CLASS E1   0–6–0T

Built: 1874–83. Stroudley LBSCR design. 80 built.
B.P.: 160 lbf/sq. in.　　**Wheel dias.:** 4′ 6″　　　**T.E.:** 17 470 lbf.
Cyls.: 17″ x 24″ (I).　　　**Weight:** 44.15 tons.
Valve Gear: Stephenson.

BR	SR	LBSCR		
	B 110	110*	East Somerset Railway	Brighton 1877

CLASS E4   0–6–2T

Built: 1897–1903. R Billinton LBSCR design. 120 built.
B.P.: 160 lbf/sq. in.　　**Wheel dias.:** 5′ 0″, 4′ 0″.　　**T.E.:** 19 090 lbf.
Cyls.: 18″ x 26″ (I).　　　**Weight:** 56.75 tons.
Valve Gear: Stephenson.

BR	SR	LBSCR			
32473	B473–2473	473*	BIRCH GROVE	Bluebell Railway	Brighton 1898

CLASS A1 & A1X   "TERRIER"   0–6–0T

Built: 1872–80 as class A1§. Stroudley LBSCR design. Most rebuilt to A1X from 1911. 50 built.
B.P.: 150 lbf/sq. in.　　**Wheel dia.:** 4′ 0″.　　**T.E.:** 10 410 lbf (8890 lbf†, 7650 lbf§).
Cyls.: 14″ (13″†, 12″§) x 20″ (I).　　**Weight:** 28.25 tons.
Valve Gear: Stephenson.
a–air brakes, d–dual brakes.

BR	SR	LBSCR			
32636*d	B 636–2636	72*	FENCHURCH	Bluebell Railway	Brighton 1872
32640a	W 11*–2640	40	NEWPORT	Isle of Wight Steam Rly.	Brighton 1878
32646a	W 2–W 8*	46–646	FRESHWATER	Isle of Wight Steam Rly.	Brighton 1876
32650d§	B 650–W 9	50*–650	WHITECHAPEL	Kent & East Sussex Rly.	Brighton 1876
DS680a§	A 751–680 S	54*–654	WADDON	Canadian Railroad Historical Museum	Brighton 1875
32655	B 655–2655	55*–655	STEPNEY	Bluebell Railway	Brighton 1875
32662*a§	B 662–2662	62–662	MARTELLO	Bressingham Gardens	Brighton 1875
32670*		70	POPLAR	Kent & East Sussex Rly.	Brighton 1872
32678d	B 678–W 4–W 14	78*–678	KNOWLE	Kent & East Sussex Rly.	Brighton 1880
a	380S	82*–682	BOXHILL	National Railway Museum	Brighton 1880

NOTE: 32640 was also named BRIGHTON. 32646 was sold to the LSWR and became 734. It has also been named NEWINGTON. 32650 became 515 S (departmental) and was named FISHBOURNE when on the Isle of Wight. It is now No. 10 SUTTON. DS 680 was sold to the SECR and became their 75. 32670 is now 3 "BODIAM" and 32678 was named BEMBRIDGE when on the Isle of Wight. 32646 was Freshwater Yarmouth and Newport Railway No. 2. 32640 was Isle of Wight Central Railway No. 11 which it now carries.

CLASS Q1   0–6–0

Built: 1942. Bulleid SR "Austerity" design. 40 built (33001–40).
B.P.: 230 lbf/sq. in.　　**Weight –Loco:** 51.25 tons.　　**Wheel dia.:** 5′ 1″.
Cyls.: 19″ x 26″ (I).　　　**–Tender:** 38 tons.　　　**T.E.:** 30 080 lbf.
Valve Gear: Stephenson.

BR	SR		
33001*	C1	Bluebell Railway (N)	Brighton 1942

CLASSES WC & BB
WEST COUNTRY and BATTLE OF BRITAIN

4–6–2

Built: 1945–51. Bulleid SR design with "air smoothed" casing, thermic syphons and Boxpox driving wheels. 110 built (34001–110).

§ Rebuilt by Jarvis 1957–61 with the removal of the air-smoothed casing.

B.P.: 250 lbf/sq. in. **Weight –Loco:** 86 (91.65§) tons. **Wheel dias.:** 3′ 1″, 6′ 2″, 3′ 1″.
Cyls.: 16⅜″ x 24″ (3). **–Tender:** 42.7, 47.9 or 47.75 tons. **T.E.:** 27 720 lbf.
Valve Gear: Bulleid chain driven (Walschaerts§).

BR	SR			
34007 *	21C107	WADEBRIDGE	Plym Valley Railway	Brighton 1945
34010§*	21C110	SIDMOUTH	Cargo Fleet, Cleveland	Brighton 1945 reb Eastleigh 1959
34016§*	21C116	BODMIN	Watercress Line	Brighton 1945 reb Eastleigh 1958
34023 *	21C123	BLACKMORE VALE	Bluebell Railway	Brighton 1946
34027§*★	21C127	TAW VALLEY	Severn Valley Railway	Brighton 1946 reb Elh 1958
34028§*	21C128	EDDYSTONE	A.J.R. Birch & Son, Sellindge	Brighton 1946 reb Elh 1959
34039§*	21C139	BOSCASTLE	Great Central Railway	Brighton 1946 reb Elh 1959
34046§*	21C146	BRAUNTON	Brighton Locomotive Works	Brighton 1946 reb Elh 1958
34051 *	21C151	WINSTON CHURCHILL	National Railway Museum	Brighton 1946
34053§*	21C153	SIR KEITH PARK	Humberside LPG, Hull	Brighton 1947 reb Eastleigh 1950
34058§*	21C158	SIR FREDERICK PILE	Avon Valley Railway	Brighton 1947 reb Eastleigh 1960
34059§*	21C159	SIR ARCHIBALD SINCLAIR	Bluebell Railway	Brighton 1947 reb Eastleigh 1960
34067 *	21C167	TANGMERE	Watercress Line	Brighton 1947
34070 *	21C170	MANSTON	Richborough Power Station	Brighton 1947
34072★		257 SQUADRON	Swanage Railway	Brighton 1948
34073		249 SQUADRON	Brighton Locomotive Works	Brighton 1948
34081		92 SQUADRON	Nene Valley Railway	Brighton 1948
34092		CITY OF WELLS	Keighley & Worth Valley Railway	Brighton 1949
34101§		HARTLAND	Great Central Railway	Eastleigh 1950 reb 1960
34105		SWANAGE	Watercress Line	Brighton 1950

Notes:

34010 will be restored as "34109 SIR TRAFFORD LEIGH–MALLORY"
34023 was named BLACKMOOR VALE to 4/50. 34092 was named WELLS to 3/50.
34027 is on loan to the North Yorkshire Moors Railway for the summer of 1991.
34051 is under repair at Swindon Railway Engineering.
34072 is on loan to the North Yorkshire Moors Railway for the summer of 1991.

CLASS MN MERCHANT NAVY 4–6–2

Built: 1941–49. Bulleid SR design with air smoothed casing and similar features to 'WC' and 'BB'. All rebuilt 1956–59 by Jarvis to more conventional appearance. 30 built (35001–30).
B.P.: 250 lbf/sq. in. **Weight –Loco:** 97.9 tons. **Wheel dias.:** 3′ 1″, 6′ 2″, 3′ 7″.
Cyls.: 18″ x 24″ (3). **–Tender:** 47.8 tons. **T.E.:** 33 490 lbf.
Valve Gear: Walschaerts.

§ Sectioned.

BR	SR			
35005*	21C5	CANADIAN PACIFIC	Great Central Railway	Eastleigh 1941 reb 1959
35006*	21C6	PENINSULAR & ORIENTAL S.N. Co.	Glos.–Warwickshire Rly	Eastleigh 1942 reb 1957
35009*	21C9	SHAW SAVILL	Brighton Locomotive Works	Eastleigh 1942 reb 1957
35010*	21C10	BLUE STAR	Royal Victoria Dock, London	Elh. 1942 reb 1957
35011*	21C11	GENERAL STEAM NAVIGATION	Brighton Locomotive Works	Eastleigh 1944 reb 1959
35018*	21C18	BRITISH INDIA LINE	Watercress Line	Eastleigh 1945 reb 1956
35022		HOLLAND–AMERICA LINE	Swanage Railway	Eastleigh 1948 reb 1956
35025		BROCKLEBANK LINE	Great Central Railway	Eastleigh 1948 reb 1956
35027		PORT LINE	Bluebell Railway	Eastleigh 1948 reb 1957
35028★		CLAN LINE	Southall Railway Centre	Eastleigh 1948 reb 1959
35029§		ELLERMAN LINES	National Railway Museum	Eastleigh 1949 reb 1959

CLASS T3   4–4–0

Built: 1982–93. Adams LSWR design. 20 built
B.P.: 175 lbf/sq. in.   **Weight –Loco:** 48.55 tons.   **Wheel dias.:** 3' 7", 6' 7".
Cyls.: 19" x 26" (O).   **–Tender:** 33.2 tons.   **T.E.:** 17 670 lbf.
Valve Gear: Stephenson.

SR	LSWR			
E563–563	563*		National Railway Museum	Nine Elms 380/1893

CLASS B1   "GLADSTONES"   0–4–2

Built: 1882–91. Stroudley LBSCR design. 49 built.
B.P.: 150 lbf/sq. in.   **Weight –Loco:** 38.7 tons.   **Wheel dias.:** 6' 6", 4' 6".
Cyls.: 18¼" x 26" (I).   **–Tender:** 29.35 tons.   **T.E.:** 14 160 lbf.
Valve Gear: Stephenson. Air brakes.

SR	LBSCR				
B618	214*–618	GLADSTONE	National Railway Museum		Brighton 1882

CANTERBURY & WHITSTABLE   RAILWAY   0–4–0

Built: 1830. R. Stephenson design.
B.P.: lbf/sq. in.   **Weight –Loco:**   **Wheel dias.:** 4' 0".
Cyls.: 10½" x 18" (O).   **–Tender:**   **T.E.:**

INVICTA	Canterbury Heritage Centre	RS24/1830

ELECTRIC LOCOMOTIVE

LSWR   Bo

Built: 1898. Siemens design for operation on the Waterloo & City line.
System: 750 V dc third rail.
Traction Motors: Two Siemens 45 kW (60 hp).
Wheel dia.: 3' 4".

BR	SR	LSWR		
DS 75	75 S*		National Railway Museum	SM6/1898

DIESEL LOCOMOTIVES

BR   CLASS 12   0–6–0

Built: 1949–52. Based on pre-war LMS design. 26 built.
Engine: English Electric 6KT of 350 hp at 680 rpm.
Traction Motors: Two EE 506A axle-hung.
Power at Rail: 163 kW (218 hp).
Max. T.E.: 107 kN (24 000 lbf).   **Weight:** 45 tonnes.
Cont. T.E.: 36 kN (8000 lbf) at 10.2 mph.   **Wheel Dias:** 1370 mm.
Max. Speed: 27 mph.

15224	Lavender Line, Isfield	Ashford 1949

ELECTRIC MULTIPLE UNITS

1285 CLASS (later 3 Sub)   DMBT

Built: 1925. Normal formation. DMBS–TS–DMBS.
Traction Motors: Two MV 167 kW (225 hp).
Max. Speed: 75 mph.
DMBS

S 8143 S	(ex. unit 1293 later 4308)	National Railway Museum	MCW 1925

4 Cor   "NELSONS"   PORTSMOUTH EXPRESS STOCK

Built: 1937–38. Normal formation. DMBSO–TSK–TCK–DMBSO.
Traction Motors: Two MV 167 kW (225 hp) per power car.
Max. Speed: 75 mph.

DMBSO	19.54 x 2.88 m	46.5 tons	52S
TSK	19.54 x 2.85 m	32.65 tons	68S
TCK	19.54 x 2.85 m	32.6 tons	30F 24S

§–Used as hauled stock.

S 10096 S	TSK	(Ex. unit 3142)	Brighton Locomotive Works	Eastleigh 1937
S 11161 S	DMBSO	(Ex. unit 3142)	Brighton Locomotive Works	Eastleigh 1937
S 11179 S	DMBSO	(Ex. unit 3131)	National Railway Museum	Eastleigh 1937
S 11187 S§	DMBSO	(Ex. unit 3135)	Nene Valley Railway	Eastleigh 1937
S 11201 S	DMBSO	(Ex. unit 3142)	Brighton Locomotive Works	Eastleigh 1937
S 11773 S§	TCK	(Ex. unit 3159)	Swanage Railway	Eastleigh 1937
S 11825 S	TCK	(Ex. unit 3135)	Brighton Locomotive Works	Eastleigh 1937

2 Bil   SEMI-FAST UNITS

Built: 1937. Normal formation DMBSK–DTCK.
Traction Motors: Two EE of 205 kW (275 hp).
Max. Speed: 75 mph.

DMBSK	19.24 x 2.85 m	43.5 tons	52S
DTCK	19.24 x 2.85 m	31.25 tons	24F 30S

S 10656 S	DMBSK	(Unit 2090 (1890))	BR, Brighton T&RSMD (N)	Eastleigh 1937
S 12123 S	DTCK	(Unit 2090 (1890))	BR, Brighton T&RSMD (N)	Eastleigh 1937

4 Buf

Built: 1937. Normal formation. DMBSO–TCK–TRBS–DMBSO.
Max. Speed: 75 mph.

TRBS	19.60 x 2.84 m	37 tons	26S

S 12529 S	TRBS	(Ex. Unit 3084)	Nene Valley Railway (N)	Eastleigh 1938

4 DD   DOUBLE DECK SUBURBAN UNITS

Built: 1949. Normal formation DMBS–TS–TS–DMBS.
Traction Motors: Two EE of 185 kW (250 hp).
Max. Speed: 75 mph.

DMBS	19.24 x 2.85 m	39 tons	121S
TS	19.24 x 2.85 m	28 tons	154S

S 13003 S	DMBS	(Unit 4002 (4902))	*Location unknown*	Lancing 1949
S 13004 S	DMBS	(Unit 4002 (4902))	Northampton Steam Railway	Lancing 1949
S 13503 S	TS	(Unit 4002 (4902))	*Location unknown*	Lancing 1949

PULLMAN

PULLMAN CAR COMPANY EMU STOCK

GENERAL

Pullman cars owned by the Pullman Car Company operated as parts of EMU formations on the Southern Railway (later Southern Region). In addition the three Brighton Belle EMU sets were composed entirely of Pullman vehicles.

6 Pul

Built: 1932. Six car sets incorporating one Pullman kitchen composite.
Normal formation: DMBSO–TSK–TCK–TPKC–TCK–DMBSO.
Now used as hauled stock.

TPCK	20.40 x 2.77 m	43 tons	12F 16S	
RUTH	TPCK	(Ex. 2017–3017)	Bulmers Railway Centre, Hereford	MCW 1932
BERTHA	TPCK	(Ex. 2012–3012)	Bluebell Railway	MCW 1932

5 Bel   BRIGHTON BELLE UNITS

Built: 1932. Five car all Pullman sets.
Formation: DMPBS–TPS–TPKF–TPKF–DMPBS.
Traction Motors: Four BTH of 167 kW (225 hp).

Static exhibits except §–Used as hauled stock.

HAZEL*	(S 279 S)	TPKF	(Ex. 2051–3051)	The Black Bull, Moulton, N. Yorks	MCW 1932
AUDREY§*	(S 280 S)	TPKF	(Ex. 2052–3052)	Venice–Simplon Orient Express	MCW 1932
GWEN§*	(S 281 S)	TPKF	(Ex. 2053–3053)	Venice–Simplon Orient Express	MCW 1932
DORIS*	(S 282 S)	TPKF	(Ex. 2051–3051)	CIL Storefitters, Finsbury Park	MCW 1932
MONA*	(S 283 S)	TPKF	(Ex. 2053–3053)	The Brighton Belle PH, Winsford	MCW 1932
VERA*§	(S 284 S)	TPKF	(Ex. 2052–3052)	Venice–Simplon Orient Express	MCW 1932
CAR 85*	(S 285 S)	TPS	(Ex. 2053–3053)	The Nags Head, Mickleover, Derby	MCW 1932
CAR 86§*	(S 286 S)	TPS	(Ex. 2051–3051)	Venice–Simplon Orient Express	MCW 1932
CAR 87§*	(S 287 S)	TPS	(Ex. 2052-3052)	North Norfolk Railway	MCW 1932
CAR 88§*	(S 288 S)	DMPBS	(Ex. 2051–3051)	Venice–Simplon Orient Express	MCW 1932
CAR 89†	(S 289 S*)	DMPBS	(Ex. 2051–3051)	Little Mill Inn, Rowarth, Derbys.	MCW 1932
CAR 90§*	(S 290 S)	DMPBS	(Ex. 2052–3052)	Steamtown, Carnforth	MCW 1932
CAR 91§*	(S 291 S)	DMPBS	(Ex. 2052–3052)	North Norfolk Railway	MCW 1932
CAR 92*	(S 292 S)	DMPBS	(Ex. 2053–3053)	Brighton Locomotive Works	MCW 1932
CAR 93*	(S 293 S)	DMPBS	(Ex. 2053–3053)	Brighton Locomotive Works	MCW 1932

† Now named DERBYSHIRE BELLE.

LONDON MIDLAND & SCOTTISH RLY AND CONSTITUENT COMPANIES' LOCOMOTIVES

GENERAL

The LMS was formed in 1923 by the amalgamation of the Midland Railway, London and North Western Railway (LNWR), Lancashire and Yorkshire Railway (L&Y), Caledonian Railway (CR), Glasgow and South Western Railway (GSWR) and Highland Railway (HR), plus a few smaller railways. Prior to this the North London Railway had been absorbed by the LNWR and the London, Tilbury and Southend Railway (LTSR) and been absorbed by the Midland.

NUMBERING SYSTEM

Originally number series were allocated to divisions as follows:

1– 4999	Midland Division (Midland and North Staffordshire Railway).
5000– 9999	Western Division 'A' (LNWR).
10000–13999	Western Division 'B' (L & Y).
14000–17999	Northern Division (Scottish Railways).

From 1934 onwards, all LMS standard locos and new builds were numbered in the range from 1–9999, and any locos which would have had their numbers duplicated had 20000 added to their original number.

At nationalisation 40000 was added to all LMS numbers except that locos which were renumbered in the 2xxxx series were further renumbered generally in the 58xxx series. In the following section locos are listed in order of BR number or in the position of the BR number they would have carried if they had lasted into BR days, except for very old locos which are listed at the end of the section.

CLASSIFICATION SYSTEM

LMS locos did not generally have unique class designations but were referred to by their power classification which varied from 0 to 8 followed by the letters 'P' for a passenger engine and 'F' for a freight engine. Mixed traffic engines had no suffix letter, but BR used the description 'MT' to denote these.

STEAM LOCOMOTIVES

CLASS 4P   COMPOUND   4–4–0

Built: 1902–03. Johnson Midland design, rebuilt by Deeley 1914–19 to a similar design to the Deeley compounds which were built 1905–09. A further similar batch was built by the LMS in 1924–32. 240 built (41000–41199, 40900–40939).
B.P.: 200 lb/sq. in.   **Weight –Loco:** 61.7 tons.   **Wheel dias.:** 3' 6½", 7' 0".
T.E.: 23 205 lbf.   **–Tender:** 45.9 tons.
Cyls.: One high pressure. 19" x 26" (I).
       Two low pressure. 21" x 26" (O).
Valve Gear: Stephenson.

BR	LMS	MR		
41000	1000	1000*(2361 pre 1907)	National Railway Museum	Derby 1902 reb 1914

CLASS 2MT   2–6–2T

Built: 1946–52. Ivatt LMS design. 130 built (41200–41329).
B.P.: 200 lb/sq. in.   **Wheel dias.**: 3' 0", 5' 0", 3' 0".   **T.E.**: 18 510 (17 410§) lbf.
Cyls.: 16½" (16"§) x 24" (O).   **Weight**: 65.2 (63.25§) tons.
Valve Gear: Walschaerts.

41241§	Keighley & Worth Valley Railway	Crewe 1949
41298	Buckinghamshire Railway Centre	Crewe 1951
41312	Caerphilly Railway Society	Crewe 1952
41313	Buckinghamshire Railway Centre	Crewe 1952

CLASS 1F   0–6–0T

Built: 1874–92. Johnson Midland design. Rebuilt with Belpaire boiler. 262 built.
B.P.: 150 lb/sq. in.   **Wheel dias.**: 4' 6½".   **T.E.**: 16 230 lbf.
Cyls.: 17" x 24" (I).   **Weight**: 45.45 tons.
Valve Gear: Stephenson.

BR	LMS	MR		
41708	1708*	1708	Swanage Railway	Derby 1880

LTS 79 CLASS (3P)   4–4–2T

Built: 1909. Whitelegg LTSR design. 4 built.
B.P.: 170 lb/sq. in.   **Wheel dias.**: 3', 6", 6' 6", 3' 6".   **T.E.**: 17 390 lbf.
Cyls.: 19" x 26" (O).   **Weight**: 69.35 tons.
Valve Gear: Stephenson.

BR	LMS	MR	LTSR			
41966	2148	2177	80* THUNDERSLEY	Bressingham Gardens (N)		RS 3367/1909

CLASS 4MT   2–6–4T

Built: 1945–51. Fairburn modification of Stanier design (built 1936–43). This in turn was a development of a Fowler design built 1927–4. 383 built (Stanier & Fairburn). (42030–299/425–94/537–699).
B.P.: 200 lb/sq. in.   **Wheel dias.**: 3', 3½", 5' 9", 3' 3½".   **T.E.**: 24 670 lbf.
Cyls.: 19⅝" x 26" (O).   **Weight**: 85.25 tons.
Valve Gear: Walschaerts.

BR	Present		
42073	2073	Lakeside & Haverthwaite Railway	Brighton 1950
42085*		Lakeside & Haverthwaite Railway	Brighton 1951

CLASS 4MT   2–6–4T

Built: 1934. Stanier LMS 3-cylinder design for LTS line. 37 built (42500–36).
B.P.: 200 lb/sq. in.   **Wheel dias.**: 3', 3½", 5' 9", 3' 3½".   **T.E.**: 24 600 lbf.
Cyls.: 16" x 26" (3).   **Weight**: 92.5 tons.
Valve Gear: Walschaerts.

BR	LMS		
42500	2500*	Bressingham Gardens (N)	Derby 1934

CLASS 5MT   "CRAB"   2–6–0

Built: 1926–32. Hughes LMS design. 245 built (42700–944).
B.P.: 180 lb/sq. in.   **Weight –Loco**: 66 tons.   **Wheel dias.**: 3' 6½", 5' 6".
Cyls.: 21" x 26" (O).   **–Tender**: 42.2 (41.5§) tons.   **T.E.**: 26 580 lbf.
Valve Gear: Walschaerts.

BR	LMS		
42700	13000–2700*	National Railway Museum	Horwich 1926
42765§*	13065–2765	Keighley & Worth Valley Raiway	Crewe 5757/1927
42859*	13159–2859	Humberside LPG Hull	Crewe 5981/1930

42765 is under restoration at Derek Foster Engineering, Kirkby, Merseyside.

CLASS 5MT   2–6–0

Built: 1933–34. Stanier LMS design. 40 built (42945–84).
B.P.: 225 lb/sq. in.   **Weight –Loco:** 69.1 tons.   **Wheel dias.:** 3′ 3½″, 5′ 6″.
Cyls.: 18″ x 28″ (O).   **–Tender:** 42.2 tons.   **T.E.:** 26 290 lbf.
Valve Gear: Walschaerts.

BR	LMS		
42968*	13268–2968	Severn Valley Railway	Crewe 1934

CLASS 4MT   2–6–0

Built: 1947–52. Ivatt design. 162 built (43000–161).
B.P.: 225 lb/sq. in.   **Weight –Loco:** 59.1 tons.   **Wheel dias.:** 3′ 0″, 5′ 3″.
Cyls.: 17½″ x 26″ (O).   **–Tender:** 40.3 tons.   **T.E.:** 24 170 lbf.
Valve Gear: Walschaerts.

43106★	Severn Valley Railway	Darlington 2148/1951

CLASS 4F   0–6–0

Built: 1911–41. Fowler Midland design. Locos from 44027 onwards were LMS locos with higher sided tenders. The preserved Midland loco has an LMS tender. 772 built (43835–44606).
B.P.: 175 lb/sq. in.   **Weight –Loco:** 48.75 tons.   **Wheel dia.:** 5′ 3″.
Cyls.: 20″ x 26″ (I).   **–Tender:** 41.2 tons.   **T.E.:** 24 560 lbf.
Valve Gear: Stephenson.

BR	LMS	MR		
43924*	3942	3924	Keighley & Worth Valley Railway	Derby 1920
44027	4027*		Midland Railway Centre (N)	Derby 1924
44123*	4123		Avon Valley Railway	Crewe 5658/1925
44422*	4422		North Staffordshire Railway	Derby 1927

CLASS 5MT   "BLACK   5"   4–6–0

Built: 1934–50. Stanier design. 842 built (44658–45499).
B.P.: 225 lb/sq. in.   **Weight –Loco:** 72.1 (75.3§) tons.   **Wheel dias.:** 3′ 3½″, 6′ 0″
Cyls.: 18½″ x 28″ (O).   **–Tender:** 53.65 (53.8§) tons.   **T.E.:** 25 450 lbf.
Valve Gear: Walschaerts (Outside Stephenson§).

BR	LMS			
44767§	4767*★	"GEORGE STEPHENSON"	North Yorkshire Moors Railway	Crewe 1947
44806*	4806	"MAGPIE"	Gtr. Manchester Museum of Sc. & I.	Derby 1944
44871*	4871	"SOVEREIGN"	Bo'ness & Kinneil Railway	Crewe 1945
44901*	4901		Butetown Historic Railway Soc.	Crewe 1945
44932*	4932★		Midland Railway Centre	Horwich 1945
45000	5000*		Steamtown Carnforth (N)	Crewe 216/1935
45025	5025*		Strathspey Railway	VF 4570/1934
45110*	5110	"RAF BIGGIN HILL"	Severn Valley Railway	VF 4653/1935
45163*	5163		Humberside LPG, Hull	AW 1204/1935
45212*	5212		Keighley & Worth Valley Railway	AW 1253/1935
45231	5231*		Nene Valley Railway	AW 1286/1936
45293*	5293		North Woolwich Station Yard	AW 1348/1936
45305	5305*★		Humberside LPG, Hull	AW 1360/1937
45337*	5337		East Lancashire Railway	AW 1392/1937
45379*	5379		Avon Valley Railway	AW 1434/1937
45407*	5407*★		Steamtown Carnforth	AW 1462/1937
45428*	5428*	"ERIC TREACY"	North Yorkshire Moors Railway	AW 1483/1937
45491*	5491		Fleetwood Locomotive Centre	Derby 1943

44767 is at present under restoration at Ian Storey Engineering, Morpeth, Northumberland.
44871 and 5305 will work from BR Fort William depot during the summer of 1991.

CLASS 6P (Formerly 5XP)   JUBILEE   4–6–0

Built: 1934–36. Stanier taper boiler development of Patriot class. 191 built (45552–45742).
B.P.: 225 lb/sq. in.   **Weight –Loco:** 79.55 tons.   **Wheel dias.:** 3′ 3½″, 6′ 9″.
Cyls.: 17″ x 26″ (3).   **–Tender:** 53.65 tons.   **T.E.:** 26 610 lbf.
Valve Gear: Walschaerts.

§ Fitted with double chimney.

BR	LMS			
45593	5593*	KOLHAPUR	Great Central Railway	NBL 24151/1934
45596*	5596§★	BAHAMAS	Keighley & Worth Valley Railway	NBL 24154/1935
45690	5690*	LEANDER	Severn Valley Railway	Crewe 288/1936
45699*	5699	GALATEA	Severn Valley Railway	Crewe 297/1936

45593 is on loan from the Birmingham Railway Museum.

CLASS 7P (Formerly 6P) ROYAL SCOT 4–6–0

Built: 1927–30. Fowler parallel design. All rebuilt 1943–55 with taper boilers and curved smoke deflectors. 71 built (46100–70).
B.P.: 250 lb/sq. in. **Weight –Loco:** 83 tons. **Wheel dias.:** 3' 3½", 6' 9".
Cyls.: 18" x 26" (3). **–Tender:** 54.65 tons. **T.E.:** 33 150 lbf.
Valve Gear: Walschaerts.

BR	LMS			
46100	6100*§	ROYAL SCOT	Bressingham Gardens (N)	Derby 1930 reb Crewe 1947
46115	6115*	SCOTS GUARDSMAN	Birmingham Rly. Mus.	NBL 23610/1927 reb Crewe 1950

§–Built as 6152 THE KING'S DRAGOON GUARDSMAN. This loco swapped identities permanently with 6100 ROYAL SCOT in 1933 for a tour of the USA.

CLASS 8P (Formerly 7P) PRINCESS ROYAL 4–6–2

Built: 1933–35. Stanier design. 13 built (46200–12).
B.P.: 250 lb/sq. in. **Weight –Loco:** 105.5 tons. **Wheel dias.:** 3' 3½", 6' 9".
Cyls.: 16¼" x 28" (4). **–Tender:** 54.65 tons. **T.E.:** 40 290 lbf.
Valve Gear: Walschaerts.

BR	LMS			
46201	6201*★	PRINCESS ELIZABETH	Bulmers Railway Centre	Crewe 107/1933
46203*★	6203	PRINCESS MARGARET ROSE	Midland Railway Centre	Crewe 253/1935

CLASS 8P (Formerly 7P) CORONATION 4–6–2

Built: 1937–48. Stanier design. 24 of this class were built streamlined but had the casing removed later. Certain locos were built with single chimneys, but all finished up with double chimneys. The tenders were fitted with steam driven coal-pushers. 38 built (46220–57).
B.P.: 250 lb/sq. in. **Weight –Loco:** 105.25 tons. **Wheel dias.:** 3' 0", 6' 9", 3' 9".
Cyls.: 16½" x 28" (4). **–Tender:** 56.35 tons. **T.E.:** 40 000 lbf.
Valve Gear: Walschaerts.

d–Formerly streamlined. Built with double chimney. Casing removed.
n–Never streamlined. Built with single chimney.
s–Formerly streamlined. Built with single chimney. Casing removed.

BR	LMS			
46229s*★	6229	DUCHESS OF HAMILTON	National Railway Museum	Crewe 1938
46233n	6233*	DUCHESS OF SUTHERLAND	Bressingham Gardens	Crewe 1938
46235d*	6235	CITY OF BIRMINGHAM	Birmingham Museum of Sc. & I.	Crewe 1939

CLASS 2MT 2–6–0

Built: 1946–53. Ivatt design. 128 built (46400–527).
B.P.: 200 lb/sq. in. **Weight –Loco:** 47.1 (48.45§) tons. **Wheel dias.:** 3' 0", 5' 0".
Cyls.: 16" (16½"§) x 24" (O). **–Tender:** 37.15 tons. **T.E.:** 17 410 (18 510§) lbf.
Valve Gear: Walschaerts.

BR	Present		
46428		East Lancashire Railway	Crewe 1948
46441	6441	Steamtown Carnforth	Crewe 1950
46443★		Severn Valley Railway	Crewe 1950
46447		Buckinghamshire Railway Centre	Crewe 1950
46464		Caledonian Railway	Crewe 1950
46512		Strathspey Railway	Swindon 1952
46521		Severn Valley Railway	Swindon 1953

Note: 46443 will be loaned to the Llangollen Railway for the summer of 1991.

CLASS 3F
"JINTY"
0–6–0T

Built: 1924–31. Fowler LMS development of his own Midland design. 422 built (47260–47681).
B.P.: 160 lb/sq. in. **Wheel dia.:** 4' 7". **T.E.:** 20 830 lbf.
Cyls.: 18" x 26" (I). **Weight:** 49.5 tons.
Valve Gear: Stephenson.

BR	LMS		
47279*	7119–7279	Keighley & Worth Valley Railway	VF 3736/1924
47298*	7138–7298	East Lancashire Railway	HE 1463/1924
47324*	16407–7324	Avon Valley Railway	NBL 23403/1926
47327*	16410–7327	Midland Railway Centre	NBL 23406/1926
47357*	16440–7357	Midland Railway Centre	NBL 23436/1926
47383*	16466–7383	Severn Valley Railway	VF 3954/1926
47406*	16489–7406	Great Central Railway	VF 3977/1926
47445*	16528–7445	Midland Railway Centre	HE 1529/1927
47493*	16576–7493	East Somerset Railway	VF 4195/1928
47564	16647–7564	Midland Railway Centre	HE 1580/1928

47298 is under restoration at Derek Foster Engineering, Kirkby, Merseyside.
47383 will be loaned to the North Norfolk Railway for the summer of 1991.

CLASS 8F
2–8–0

Built: 1934–46. Stanier design. Many were shipped overseas during the war. The ones shown as TCDD (Turkey) are now mostly withdrawn.
B.P.: 225 lb/sq. in. **Weight –Loco:** 72.1 tons. **Wheel dias.:** 3' 3½", ,4' 8½".
Cyls.: 18½" x 28" (O). **–Tender:** 53.65 tons. **T.E.:** 32 440 lbf.
Valve Gear: Walschaerts.
Turkish locos have air brakes. Some may now have been cut up.
†–Number allocated but never carried.
§–Became Persian Railways 41.109. WD number was 7037 in 1944 and 500 in 1952.

BR	LMS	WD	Present		
48151*★	8151			Steamtown Carnforth	Crewe 1942
48173*	8173			Avon Valley Railway	Crewe 1943
	8265†	339	45163*	TCDD	NBL 24639/1940
	8266†	340	45168*	TCDD	NBL 24640/1940
	8267†	341	45166*	TCDD	NBL 24641/1940
	8262†	342	45164*	TCDD	NBL 24642/1940
	8272†	346	45156*	TCDD	NBL 24646/1940
	8273†	347	45162*	TCDD	NBL 24647/1940
	8274†	348	45160*	Blue Circle Cement, Hamworthy Jn.	NBL 24648/1940
	8275†	349	45159*	TCDD	NBL 24649/1940
	8276†	350	45158*	TCDD	NBL 24650/1940
	8277†	351	45157*	TCDD	NBL 24651/1940
	8278†	352	45167*	TCDD	NBL 24652/1940
	8279†	353	45165*	TCDD	NBL 24653/1940
	8283†	357	45153*	TCDD	NBL 24657/1940
	8284†	358	45154*	TCDD	NBL 24658/1940
	8285†	359	45155*	TCDD	NBL 24659/1940
		522	45161*	TCDD	NBL 24670/1941
		523	45152*	TCDD	NBL 24671/1941
		524	45151*	TCDD	NBL 24672/1941
		547	1429*	IRR, Baghdad	NBL 24740/1941
		554	45170*	TCDD	NBL 24755/1942
48305*	8305			Great Central Railway	Crewe 1943
48431	8431*			Keighley & Worth Valley Railway	Swindon 1944
48518*				Butetown Historic Railway Society	Doncaster 1966/1944
48624*				Peak Railway, Darley Dale	Ashford 1943
48773	8233*	307§		Severn Valley Railway	NBL 24607/1940

CLASS 7F
0–8–0

Built: 1921–22. Beames development of 1912 Bowen-Cooke LNWR design. 60 built (49395–454). In addition many 1912 locos were rebuilt to similar condition.
B.P.: 175 lb/sq. in. **Weight –Loco:** 62 tons. **Wheel dia.:** 4' 5½".
Cyls.: 20½" x 24" (I). **–Tender:** 40.75 tons. **T.E.:** 28 040 lbf.
Valve Gear: Joy.

BR	LMS	LNWR
49395	9395*	485

Midland Railway Centre (N)　　　　　Crewe 5662/1921

L & Y CLASS 5　　　　　　　2–4–2T

Built: 1889–1909. Aspinall L & Y design (2P) 210 built.
B.P.: 180 lb/sq. in.　**Wheel dias.:** 3′ 7⅛″, 5′ 7⅝″, 3′ 7⅛″.　**T.E.:** 18 990 lbf.
Cyls.: 18″ x 26″ (I).　**Weight:** 55.45 tons.
Valve Gear: Joy.

BR	LMS	L & Y
50621	10621	1008*

National Railway Museum　　　　　Horwich 1/1889

L & Y CLASS 21　　　"PUG"　　　0–4–0ST

Built: 1891–1910. Aspinall L & Y design. (0F). 57 built.
B.P.: 160 lb/sq. in.　**Wheel dia.:** 3′ 0⅝″.　**T.E.:** 11 370 lbf.
Cyls.: 13″ x 18″ (O).　**Weight:** 21.25 tons.
Valve Gear: Stephenson.

BR	LMS	L & Y
51218*	11218	68
	11243	19*

Keighley & Worth Valley Railway　　Horwich 811/1901
Keighley & Worth Valley Railway　　Horwich 1097/1910

L & Y CLASS 23　　　　　　0–6–0ST

Built: 1891–1900. Aspinall rebuild of Barton Wright L & Y 0–6–0. 230 built.
B.P.: 140 lb/sq. in.　**Wheel dia.:** 4′ 5⅞″.　**T.E.:** 17 590 lbf.
Cyls.: 17½″ x 26″ (I).　**Weight:** 43.85 tons.
Valve Gear: Joy.

BR	LMS	L & Y
	11456	752*

Keighley & WV Railway　　BP 1989/1881 reb. Hor. 1896

L & Y CLASS 25　　　　　　0–6–0

Built: 1876–87. Barton Wright L & Y design (2F) 280 built.
B.P.: 140 lb/sq. in.　**Weight –Loco:** 39.05 tons.　**Wheel dia.:** 4′ 5⅞″.
Cyls.: 17½″ x 26″ (I).　**–Tender:** 28.5 tons.　**T.E.:** 17 590 lbf.
Valve Gear: Joy.

BR	LMS	L & Y
52044*	12044	957

Keighley & Worth Valley Railway　　　BP 2840/1887

L & Y CLASS 27　　　　　　0–6–0

Built: 1889–1917. Aspinall L & Y design (3F). 448 built.
B.P.: 180 lb/sq. in.　**Weight –Loco:** 44.3 tons.　**Wheel dia.:** 5′ 0⅞″.
Cyls.: 18″ x 26″ (I).　**–Tender:** 26.1 tons.　**T.E.:** 21 170 lbf.
Valve Gear: Joy.

BR	LMS	L & Y
52322	12322	1300*

Steamtown Carnforth　　　　　Horwich 420/1896

CLASS 7F　　　　　　　　　2–8–0

Built: 1914–25. Fowler design for Somerset & Dorset Joint Railway (Midland and LSWR jointly owned). 11 built (53800–10).
B.P.: 190 lb/sq. in.　**Weight –Loco:** 64.75 tons.　**Wheel dias.:** 3′ 3½″, 4′ 7½″.
Cyls.: 21″ x 28″ (O).　**–Tender:** 26.1 tons.　**T.E.:** 35 950 lbf.
Valve Gear: Walschaerts.

BR	SDJR	
53808*	9678–13808	88
53809*§★	9679–13809	89

West Somerset Railway　　　　RS 3894/1925
Midland Railway Centre　　　　RS 3895/1925

§–Carries name "BEAUMONT" except when on main-line duty.

CALEDONIAN RAILWAY　　　　4–2–2

Built: 1886. Drummond design (1P). 1 built.
B.P.: 160 lb/sq. in.　**Weight –Loco:** 41.35 tons.　**Wheel dias.:** 3′ 6″, 7′ 0″, 4′ 6″.
Cyls.: 18″ x 26″ (I).　**–Tender:** 35.4 tons.　**T.E.:** 13 640 lbf.

Valve Gear: Stephenson.

BR	LMS	CR		
14010	123*		Glasgow Museum of Transport (N)	N 3553/1886

CALEDONIAN RAILWAY 439 CLASS   0–4–4T

Built: 1900–14. McIntosh design (2P). 68 built.
B.P.: 160 lb/sq. in.   **Wheel dias.:** 5' 9", 3' 2".   **T.E.:** 16 600 lbf.
Cyls.: 18" x 26" (I).   **Weight:** 53.95 tons.
Valve Gear: Stephenson.
Dual brakes.

BR	LMS	CR		
55189	15189	419*	Bo'ness & Kinneil Railway	St. Rollox 1908

GSWR 322 CLASS   0–6–0T

Built: 1917. Drummond design. (3F). 3 built.
B.P.: 160 lb/sq. in.   **Wheel dia.:** 4' 2".   **T.E.:** 17 290 lbf.
Cyls.: 17" x 22" (O).   **Weight:** 40 tons.
Valve Gear: Walschaerts.

BR	LMS	GSWR		
16379	9*		Glasgow Museum of Transport (N)	NBL 21521/1917

CALEDONIAN RAILWAY 812 CLASS   0–6–0

Built: 1899–1900. McIntosh design (3F). 96 built (57550–645).
B.P.: 160 lb/sq. in.   **Weight –Loco:** 45.7 tons.   **Wheel dia.:** 5' 0".
Cyls.: 18½" x 26" (I).   **–Tender:** 37.9 tons.   **T.E.:** 20 170 lbf.
Valve Gear: Stephenson.
Air brakes.

BR	LMS	CR		
57566	17566	828*	Strathspey Railway	St. Rollox 1899

HIGHLAND RAILWAY   "JONES GOODS"   4–6–0

Built: 1894. Jones design (4F). 15 built.
B.P.: 175 lb/sq. in.   **Weight –Loco:** 56 tons.   **Wheel dias.:** 3' 3", 5' 3".
Cyls.: 20" x 26" (O).   **–Tender:** 38.35 tons.   **T.E.:** 24 560 lbf.
Valve Gear: Stephenson.

BR	LMS	HR		
17916	103*		Glasgow Museum of Transport (N)	SS 4022/1894

NORTH LONDON RAILWAY 75 CLASS   0–6–0T

Built: 1881–1905. Park design. (2F). 15 built.
B.P.: 160 lb/sq. in.   **Wheel dia.:** 4' 4".   **T.E.:** 18 140 lbf.
Cyls.: 17" x 24" (O).   **Weight:** 45.55 tons.
Valve Gear: Stephenson.

BR	LMS	LNWR	NLR		
58850*	7505–27505	2650	116	Bluebell Railway	Bow 181/1881

LNWR COAL TANK 0–6–2T

Built: 1881–1896. Webb design. 300 built.
B.P.: 150 lb/sq. in.   **Wheel dias.:** 4' 5½", 3' 9".   **T.E.:** 16 530 lbf.
Cyls.: 17" x 24" (I).   **Weight:** 43.75 tons.
Valve Gear: Stephenson.

BR	LMS	LNWR		
58926	7799	1054*★	Keighley & Worth Valley Railway (N)	Crewe 2979/1888

MIDLAND 156 CLASS   2–4–0

Built: 1866–68. Kirtley design (1P). 23 built.
B.P.: 140 lb/sq. in.   **Weight –Loco:** 41.25 tons.   **Wheel dias.:** 4' 3", 6' 3".
Cyls.: 18" x 24" (I).   **–Tender:** 34.85 tons.   **T.E.:** 12 340 lbf.
Valve Gear: Stephenson.

LMS   *MR*
2–20002   158–158A*   Midland Railway Centre (N)   Derby 1866

MIDLAND 115 CLASS   "SPINNER"   4–2–2

Built: 1887–1900. Johnson design. 95 built.
B.P.: 170 lb/sq. in.   **Weight –Loco:** 43.95 tons.   **Wheel dias.:** 3' 10", 7' 9½", 4' 4½ ".
Cyls.: 19" x 26" (I).   **–Tender:** 21.55 tons.   **T.E.:** 15 280 lbf.
Valve Gear: Stephenson.

LMS   *MR*
673   118–673*   National Railway Museum   Derby 1897

NORTH STAFFS RAILWAY New L CLASS   0–6–2T

Built: 1903–23. Hookham design. 34 built.
B.P.: 175 lb/sq. in.   **Wheel dias.:** 5' 0", 4' 0".   **T.E.:** 22 060 lbf.
Cyls.: " x " (I).   **Weight:** 64.95 tons.
Valve Gear: Stephenson.

LMS   *NSR*
2271   2*   Chatterley Whitfield Mining Museum (N)   Stoke 1923
Note: Although built in 1923, this loco carried an NSR number, since the NSR was not taken over by the LMS until late 1923.

LNWR   PRECEDENT   2–4–0

Built: 1874–82. Webb design. 166 built.
B.P.: 150 lb/sq. in.   **Weight –Loco:** 35.6 tons.   **Wheel dias.:** 3' 9", 6' 9".
Cyls.: 17" x 24" (I).   **–Tender:** 25 tons.   **T.E.:** 10 920 lbf.
Valve Gear: Allan.

LMS   *LNWR*
5031   790*   HARDWICKE   National Railway Museum   Crewe 3286/1892

LNWR   2–2–2

Built: 1847. Trevithick design rebuilt by Ramsbottom in 1858.
B.P.: 140 lb/sq. in.   **Weight –Loco:** 29.9 tons.   **Wheel dias.:** 3' 6", 8' 6", 3' 6".
Cyls.: 17¼" x 24" (O).   **–Tender:** 25 tons.   **T.E.:** 8330 lbf.
Valve Gear: Stephenson.

LNWR
173–3020* CORNWALL   BREL Ltd., Crewe Works (N)   Crewe 35/1847

LNWR   0–4–0ST

Built: 1865. Ramsbottom design.
B.P.: 120 lb/sq. in.   **Wheel dia.:** 4' 0".   **T.E.:** 8330 lbf.
Cyls.: 14" x 20" (I).   **Weight:** 22.75 tons.
1439*–1985–3042   National Railway Museum   Crewe 842/1865
This loco is at present in store at Swindon.

GRAND JUNCTION RAILWAY   2–2–2

Built: 1845. Trevithick design.
B.P.: 120 lb/sq. in.   **Weight –Loco:** 20.4 tons.   **Wheel dias.:** 3' 6", 6' 0", 3' 6".
Cyls.: 15" x 20" (O).   **–Tender:** 16.4 tons.   **T.E.:** 6375 lbf.
Valve Gear: Allan.

GJR   *LNWR*
49   49*   COLUMBINE   National Railway Museum   Crewe 25/1845
This loco is at present in store at Swindon.

FURNESS   RAILWAY   0–4–0

Built: 1846.
B.P.: 110 lb/sq. in.   **Weight –Loco:** 20 tons.   **Wheel dia.:** 4' 9".
Cyls.: 14" x 24" (I).   **–Tender:** 13 tons.   **T.E.:** 7720 lbf.
Valve Gear: Stephenson.
3   COPPERNOB   National Railway Museum   BCK 1846

FURNESS RAILWAY 0–4–0ST

Built: 1863/5.
B.P.:   **Wheel dia.:**   **T.E.:** lbf.
Cyls.: (I)   **Weight:**

FR	*Present*		
18	CHLOE	Steamtown Carnforth	SS 1435/1863
25	17	Steamtown Carnforth	SS 1585/1865

LIVERPOOL & MANCHESTER RAILWAY 0–2–2

Built: 1829 for the Rainhill trials.
B.P.: 50 lb/sq. in.   **Weight** –Loco: 4.25 tons.   **Wheel dias.:** 4' 8½", 2' 6".
Cyls.: 8" x 17" (O).   –Tender: 5.2 tons.   **T.E.:** 820 lbf.

ROCKET	Science Museum, London (N)	RS 1/1829

LIVERPOOL & MANCHESTER RAILWAY 0–4–0

Built: 1829 for the Rainhill trials.
B.P.: 50 lb/sq. in.   **Weight** –Loco: 4.25 tons.   **Wheel dias.:** 4' 6".
Cyls.: 7" x 18" (O).   –Tender: 5.2 tons.   **T.E.:** 690 lbf.

SANS PAREIL	Science Museum, London (N)	Hack 1829

LIVERPOOL & MANCHESTER RAILWAY 0–4–2

Built: 1838–9. Four built. The survivor was the star of the film "The Titfield Thunderbolt"
B.P.: 50 lb/sq. in.   **Weight** –Loco: 14.45 tons.   **Wheel dias.:** 5' 0", 3' 3".
Cyls.: 14" x 24" (I).   –Tender: 0 tons.   **T.E.:** 3330 lbf.

L & M	*LNWR*			
57	116	LION	Liverpool Museum	TKL 1838

MERSEY RAILWAY 0–6–4T

Built:
B.P.: 150 lb/sq. in.   **Wheel dias.:** 4' 7", 3' 0".   **T.E.:** 26 600 lbf.
Cyls.: 21" x 26" (I).   **Weight:** 67.85 tons.
Valve Gear: Stephenson.

1	THE MAJOR	Rail Transport Museum, Thirlemere, NSW	BP /18
5	CECIL RAIKES	Steamport Railway Museum	BP 2605/1885

LNWR 0–4–0STT

Built: 1865 for Crewe Works internal system.
B.P.:   **Wheel dias.:** 1' 4¼".   **T.E.:** lbf.
Cyls.: (I)   **Weight:** tons.   **Gauge:** 1' 6".

PET	Narrow Gauge Museum, Tywyn (N)	Crewe 6/1865

L & YR 0–4–0STT

Built: 1887 for Horwich Works internal system.
B.P.: 170 lb/sq. in.   **Wheel dias.:** 1' 4¼".**T.E.:** 1330 lbf.
Cyls.: 5" x 6" (O).   **Weight:** 3.55 tons.   **Gauge:** 1' 6".
Valve Gear: Joy.

WREN	National Railway Museum	BP 2825/1887

MIDLAND RAILWAY 0–4–0ST

Built: 1911 for Beeston Sleeper Depot internal system.
B.P.:   **Wheel dias.:**   **T.E.:**
Cyls.:   **Weight:**   **Gauge:** 3' 0".
Valve Gear: Joy.

MR	*LMS*	*BR*		
1	ED 10	ED 10	"Poplars", North Moreton	Bagnall 1889/1911

DIESEL & PETROL LOCOMOTIVES

DIESEL MECHANICAL   0-4-0

Built: 1934 by English Electric at Preston Works for Drewry Car Co.
Engine: Allan 8RS18 of 119 kW (160 hp) at 1200 rpm. (Now fitted with a Gardner 6L3 of 114 kW (153 hp.).
Transmission: Wilson four-speed gearbox driving a rear jackshaft.
Max. T.E.: 50 kN (15300 lbf).   **Weight:** tonnes.
Max. Speed: 12 mph.   **Wheel Dia:** 914 mm.

LMS	WD			
7050	AD 240 "RORKE'S DRIFT"	Museum of Army Transport, Beverley	DC 2047/EE 847/1934

DIESEL MECHANICAL   0-6-0

Built: 1932 by Hunslet Engine Co. (taken into stock 1933).
Engine: MAN 112 kW (150 hp) at 900 rpm. (Now fitted with a Maclaren/Ricardo 98 kW engine).
Transmission: Hunslet constant mesh four-speed gearbox.
Max. T.E.: 33 kN.   **Weight:** 21.7 tonnes.
Max. Speed: 30 mph.   **Wheel Dia:** 914 mm.

7051–7401*	"JOHN ALCOCK"	Middleton Railway (N)	HE 1697/1933

DIESEL ELECTRIC   0-6-0

Built: 1939–42 at Derby. 11 built, 3 taken over by BR as 12000–2 (LMS 7074/6/9). Scrapped 1956–62. Others sold to WD for France.
Engine: English Electric 6KT of 261 kW (350 hp) at 675 rpm.
Transmission: One traction motor.
Max. T.E.: 147 kN (33000 lbf).   **Weight:** 52 tonnes.
Max Speed: 30 mph.   **Wheel Dia:** 1232 mm.

LMS	WD		
7069*	18	Swanage Railway	Derby 1941

DIESEL ELECTRIC   0-6-0

Built: 1939–42 at Derby. 40 built, 30 taken over by BR as 12003–32 (LMS 7080–99, 7110–9). Scrapped 1964–7. Others sold to WD for Italy and Egypt.
Engine: English Electric 6KT of 261 kW (350 hp) at 680 rpm.
Transmission: One traction motor with jackshaft drive.
Max. T.E.: 147 kN (33000 lbf).   **Weight:** 56 tonnes.
Max Speed: **Wheel Dia:** 1295 mm.

LMS	WD	FS		
7103	52	700.001	FSAS, Stialunga, Italy	Derby 1941
7106	55	700.003	FSAS, Stialunga, Italy	Derby 1941

BR CLASS 11   DIESEL ELECTRIC   0-6-0

Built: 1945–53. LMS design. 106 built.
Engine: English Electric 6KT of 261 kW (350 hp) at 680 rpm.
Traction Motors: Two EE 506 axle hung.
Power at Rail: 183 kW (245 hp).
Max. T.E.: 156 kN (35000 lbf).   **Weight:** 56 tonnes.
Cont. T.E.: 49.4 kN (11100 lbf) at 8.8 mph.   **Wheel Dia:** 1372 mm.
Max. Speed: 20 mph.

BR	Present		
12049	None	Day & Sons Brentford Town Goods Depot	Derby 1948
12052	MP228	Scottish Industrial Railway Centre	Derby 1949
12061	4	Vale of Neath Railway, Cadoxton Site	Derby 1949
12071	6	Booth-Roe Metals, Rotherham	Derby 1950
12074		South Yorkshire Railway	Derby 1950
12077		Midland Railway Centre	Derby 1950
12082		Kemira Fertilisers, Ince Marshes, Cheshire	Derby 1950
12083	201276	Tilcon, Grassington	Derby 1950
12088		South Yorkshire Railway	Derby 1951
12093	MP229	Scottish Industrial Railway Centre	Derby 1951
12098	513	North Tyneside Railway	Derby 1952
12099		Severn Valley Railway	Derby 1952
12131		North Norfolk Railway	Darlington 1952

L & YR PETROL   4w

Built: 1919 by Motor Rail & Tram Car Co. for departmental use.
Engine: Dorman 4JO of 30 kW (40 hp).
Transmission: Dixon Abbott two-speed gearbox with forward & reverse chain drive to axles.
Max. T.E.: 17 kN (3750 lbf).   **Weight:** 8 tonnes.
Max. Speed: 7 mph.   **Wheel Dia:** 940 mm.

| 1 | Chasewater Light Railway | MR 1947/1919 |

BATTERY ELECTRIC LOCOMOTIVE

NSR   4w

Built: 1917.
Battery: 108 cells giving an output of 61 kW (82 hp).
Transmission: Wilson four-speed gearbox driving a rear jackshaft.
Max. T.E.: 50 kN (15300 lbf).   **Wheel Dia:** 940 mm.

NSR	LMS			
2*	BEL 2		National Railway Museum	1917

ELECTRIC MULTIPLE UNITS

LNWR OERLIKON STOCK

Built: 1915. Normal formation: DMBTO–TTO–DTTO. 630 V dc third rail. Used on Euston–Watford line.
Traction Motors: Four Oerlikon 179 kW (240 hp).
Max. Speed:
| DMBTO | 17.60 x 2.73 m | 54.75 tonnes. | 48T |

BR	LMS			
M 28249	M 28249*	DMBSO	National Railway Museum	MCW 1915

CLASS 502   LIVERPOOL–SOUTHPORT STOCK

Built: 1939. Normal formation: DMBSO–TSO–DTSO. 630V dc third rail.
Traction Motors: Four EE 175 kW traction motors.   **Max. Speed:** 65 mph.
| DMBSO | 20.26 x 2.90 m | 42.5 tonnes. | 88S |
| DTSO | 20.26 x 2.90 m | 25.5 tonnes. | 79S |

BR	LMS			
M 28361	M 28361*	DMBSO	Steamport Railway Museum (N)	Derby 1939
M 29896	M 29896*	DTSO	Steamport Railway Museum (N)	Derby 1939

CLASS 503   MERSEY–WIRRAL STOCK

Built: 1938. Normal formation: DMBSO–TSO–DTSO. 630V dc third rail.
Traction Motors: 4 BTH 100 kW.   **Max. Speed:** 65 mph.
DMBSO	17.68 x 2.77 m	36.5 tonnes.	56S
TSO	17.07 x 2.77 m	20.5 tonnes.	58S
DTSO	17.68 x 2.77 m	21.5 tonnes.	66S

BR	LMS			
M 28690	M 28690*	DMBSO	Wirral BC, Birkenhead	Derby 1938
M 29720	M 29720*	TSO	Wirral BC, Birkenhead	Derby 1938
M 29289	M 29289*	DTSO	Wirral BC, Birkenhead	Derby 1938

MSJ&A STOCK

Built: 1939. Normal formation: DMBS–TC–DTS. 1500V dc overhead. used on Manchester South Junction and Altrincham line until it was converted to 25 kV ac.
Traction Motors: **Max. Speed:**   mph.
| TC | 17.60 x 2.85 m | 31 tonnes. | 24F 72S |

BR	LMS			
M 29663	M 29663	TC	Midland Railway Centre	MCW 1931
M 29666	M 29666	TC	Midland Railway Centre	MCW 1931
M 29670	M 29670	TC	Midland Railway Centre	MCW 1931

LONDON & NORTH EASTERN RAILWAY AND CONSTITUENT COMPANIES' LOCOMOTIVES

GENERAL

The LNER was formed in 1923 by the amalgamation of the Great Northern Railway (GNR). North Eastern Railway (NER), Great Eastern Railway (GER), Great Central Railway (GCR), North British Railway (NBR), Great North of Scotland Railway (GNSR) and Hull and Barnsley Railway (H & B).

LOCOMOTIVE NUMBERING SYSTEM

Initially pre grouping loco numbers were retained, but in September 1923 suffix letters started to be applied depending upon the works which repaired the locos. In 1924 locos were renumbered in blocks as follows: NER locos remained unaltered, GNR locos had 3000 added, GCR 5000, GNSR 6800, GER 7000 and NBR 9000. New locos filled in gaps in existing numbers. By 1943 the numbering of new locos had become so haphazard that it was decided to completely renumber locos so that locos of a particular class were all contained in the same block of numbers. On nationalisation in 1948, 60000 was added to LNER numbers.

CLASSIFICATION SYSTEM

The LNER gave each class a unique code consisting of a letter denoting the wheel arrangement and a number denoting the individual class within the wheel arrangement. Route availability (RA) was denoted by a number, the higher the number the more restricted the route availability.

STEAM LOCOMOTIVES

CLASS A4   4–6–2

Built: 1935–38. Gresley streamlined design. 'MALLARD' attained the world speed record for a steam locomotive of 126.4 mph in 1938 and is still unbeaten. 35 built (60001–34).
B.P.: 250 lb/sq. in.   **Weight –Loco:** 102.95 tons.   **Wheel dias.:** 3' 2", 6' 8", 3' 8".
Cyls.: 18½" x 26" (3).   **–Tender:** 64.15 tons.   **T.E.:** 35 450 lbf.
Valve Gear: Walschaerts with derived motion for inside cylinder.
RA: 9.

BR	LNER			
60007	4498*★–7	SIR NIGEL GRESLEY	Steamtown Carnforth	Doncaster 1863/1937
60008*	4496–8	DWIGHT D. EISENHOWER	National RR Mus., USA	Doncaster 1861/1937
60009*★4488–9		UNION OF SOUTH AFRICA	Markinch Goods Depot	Doncaster 1853/1937
60010*	4489–10	DOMINION OF CANADA	Canadian RR Hist. Mus.	Doncaster 1854/1937
60019	4464–19	BITTERN	North Tyneside Railway	Doncaster 1866/1937
60022	4468*★–22	MALLARD	National Railway Museum	Doncaster 1870/1937

60009 carries the name "OSPREY". This was originally allocated to this loco but never previously carried. 60019 has been restored as LNER "2509 SILVER LINK".

CLASS A3   4–6–2

Built: 1922–35. Gresley design (Originally class A1–later altered to A10). 79 built. (60035–113).

B.P.: 220 lb/sq. in.   **Weight –Loco**: 96.25 tons.   **Wheel dias.**: 3′ 2″, 6′ 8″, 3′ 8″.
Cyls.: 19″ x 26″ (3).   **–Tender**: 62.4 tons.   **T.E.**: 32 910 lbf.
Valve Gear: Walschaerts with derived motion for inside cylinder.
RA: 9.

BR   LNER
60103 1472–4472*★–502–103 FLYING SCOTSMAN
                      Southall Railway Centre   Doncaster 1564/1923

CLASS A2   4–6–2

Built: 1944–48. Thompson design, later developed by Peppercorn. 40 built (60500–39).
B.P.: 250 lb/sq. in.   **Weight –Loco**: 101 tons.   **Wheel dias.**: 3′ 2″, 6′ 2″, 3′ 8″.
Cyls.: 19″ x 26″ (3).   **–Tender**: 60.35 tons.   **T.E.**: 40 430 lbf.
Valve Gear: Walschaerts.   **RA**: 9.

60532   BLUE PETER   ICI Wilton, Middlesbrough   Doncaster 2023/1948

CLASS V2   2–6–2

Built: 1936–44. Gresley design for express passenger and freight. 184 built (60800–983).
B.P.: 220 lb/sq. in.   **Weight –Loco**: 93.1 tons.   **Wheel dias.**: 3′ 2″, 6′ 2″, 3′ 8″.
Cyls.: 18½″ x 26″ (3).   **–Tender**: 52 tons.   **T.E.**: 33 730 lbf.
Valve Gear: Walschaerts with derived motion for inside cylinder.
RA: 9.

BR   LNER
60800 4771*★–800 GREEN ARROW   National Railway Museum   Doncaster 1837/1936

CLASS B1   4–6–0

Built: 1942–51. Thompson design. 410 built (61000–409).
B.P.: 225 lb/sq. in.   **Weight –Loco**: 71.15 tons.   **Wheel dias.**: 3′ 2″, 6′ 2″.
Cyls.: 20″ x 26″ (O).   **–Tender**: 52 tons.   **T.E.**: 26 880 lbf.
Valve Gear: Walschaerts.   **RA**: 5.

BR   LNER Present
61264* 1264   Great Central Railway   NBL 26165/1947
61306   1306 "MAYFLOWER"   Humberside LPG, Hull   NBL 26207/1948

Notes: The original MAYFLOWER was 61379. 61264 also carried Departmental 29.

CLASS B12   4–6–0

Built: 1911–28. Holden GER design. 80 built (61500–80). GER class S69.
B.P.: 180 lb/sq. in.   **Weight –Loco**: 69.5 tons.   **Wheel dias.**: 3′ 3″, 6′ 6″, 4′ 1″.
Cyls.: 20″ x 28″ (I).   **–Tender**: 39.3 tons.   **T.E.**: 21 970 lbf.
Valve Gear: Stephenson.   **RA**: 5.   Dual brakes.

BR   LNER
61572* 8572 1572   North Norfolk Railway   BP 6488/1928

CLASS K4   2–6–0

Built: 1937–38. Gresley design for West Highland line. 6 built (61993–8).
B.P.: 200 lb/sq. in.   **Weight –Loco**: 68.4 tons.   **Wheel dias.**: 3′ 2″, 5′ 2″.
Cyls.: 18½″ x 26″ (3).   **–Tender**: 44.2 tons.   **T.E.**: 36 600 lbf.
Valve Gear: Walschaerts with derived motion for inside cylinder.
RA: 6.

BR   LNER
61994★ 3442*–1994 THE GREAT
                MARQUESS   Severn Valley Railway   Darlington 1761/1938

CLASS K1   2–6–0

Built: 1949–50. Peppercorn design. 70 built (62001–70).
B.P.: 225 lb/sq. in.   **Weight –Loco**: 66 tons.   **Wheel dias.**: 3′ 2″, 5′ 2″.
Cyls.: 20″ x 26″ (O).   **–Tender**: 52.2 tons.   **T.E.**: 32 080 lbf.
Valve Gear: Walschaerts.   **RA**: 6.

BR   Present
62005 2005★   North Yorkshire Moors Railway   NBL 26609/1949

CLASS D40   4–4–0

Built: 1889–1921. Pickersgill GNSR class F. 20 built.
B.P.: 165 lb/sq. in.   **Weight –Loco**: 48.65 tons.   **Wheel dias.**: 3' 9½", 6' 1".
Cyls.: 18" x 26" (I).   **–Tender**: 37.4 tons.   **T.E.**: 16 180 lbf.
Valve Gear: Stephenson.   **RA**: 4.

BR   LNER   GNSR
62277 6849–2277   49*   GORDON
                HIGHLANDER   Glasgow Museum of Transport (N)   NBL 22563/1920

CLASS D34   GLEN   4–4–0

Built: 1913–20. Reid NBR class K. 32 built.
B.P.: 165 lb/sq. in.   **Weight –Loco**: 57.2 tons.   **Wheel dias.**: 3' 6", 6' 0".
Cyls.: 20" x 26" (I).   **–Tender**: 46.65 tons.   **T.E.**: 22 100 lbf.
Valve Gear: Stephenson.   **RA**: 6.

BR   LNER   NBR
62469 9256–2469   256* GLEN DOUGLAS Glasgow Museum of Transport (N)   Cowlairs 1913

CLASS D11   IMPROVED DIRECTOR   4–4–0

Built: 1919–22. Robinson GCR class 11F. 11 built (62660–70). 24 similar locos were built by the LNER.
B.P.: 180 lb/sq. in.   **Weight –Loco**: 61.15 tons.   **Wheel dias.**: 3' 6", 6' 9".
Cyls.: 20" x 26" (I).   **–Tender**: 48.3 tons.   **T.E.**: 19 640 lbf.
Valve Gear: Stephenson.   **RA**: 6.

BR   LNER   GCR
62660 5506–2660   506* BUTLER
                HENDERSON   Great Central Railway (N)   Gorton 1919

CLASS D49   4–4–0

Built: 1927. Gresley design. 76 built (62700–75).
B.P.: 180 lb/sq. in.   **Weight –Loco**: 66 tons.   **Wheel dias.**: 3' 1¼", 6' 8".
Cyls.: 17" x 26" (3).   **–Tender**: 52 tons.   **T.E.**: 21 560 lbf.
Valve Gear: Walschaerts.   **RA**: 8.

BR   LNER
62712 246*–2712   MORAYSHIRE   Bo'ness & Kinneil Railway   Darlington 1391/1928

CLASS E4   2–4–0

Built: 1891–1902. Holden GER class T26. 100 built.
B.P.: 160 lb/sq. in.   **Weight –Loco**: 40.3 tons.   **Wheel dias.**: 4' 0", 5' 8".
Cyls.: 17½" x 24" (I).   **–Tender**: 30.65 tons.   **T.E.**: 14 700 lbf.
Valve Gear: Stephenson.   **RA**: 2.   Air brakes.

BR   LNER   GER
62785 7490–7802–2785 490*   Bressingham Gardens (N)   Stratford 836/1894

CLASS C1   4–4–2

Built: 1902–10. Ivatt GNR class C1. 94 built.
B.P.: 170 lb/sq. in.   **Weight –Loco**: 69.6 tons.   **Wheel dias.**: 3' 8", 6' 8", 3' 8".
Cyls.: 20" x 24" (O).   **–Tender**: 43.1 tons.   **T.E.**: 17 340 lbf.
Valve Gear: Stephenson.   **RA**: 7.

BR   LNER   GNR
     3251–2800   251*   National Railway Museum   Doncaster 991/1902

CLASS Q6   0–8–0

Built: 1913–21. Raven NER class T2. 120 built (63340–459).
B.P.: 180 lb/sq. in.   **Weight –Loco**: 65.9 tons.   **Wheel dia.**: 4' 7¼".
Cyls.: 20" x 26" (O).   **–Tender**: 44.1 tons.   **T.E.**: 28 800 lbf.
Valve Gear: Stephenson.   **RA**: 6.

BR   LNER   NER
63395 2238–3395   2238*   North Yorkshire Moors Railway   Darlington 1918

CLASS Q7   0–8–0

Built: 1919–24. Raven NER class T3. 15 built (63460–74).
B.P.: 180 lb/sq. in.   **Weight –Loco:** 71.6 tons.   **Wheel dia.:** 4' 7¼".
Cyls.: 18½" x 26" (3).   **–Tender:** 44.1 tons.   **T.E.:** 36 960 lbf.
Valve Gear: Stephenson.   **RA:** 7.

BR   LNER   NER
63460*   901–3460   901   North Yorkshire Moors Railway (N)   Darlington 1919

CLASS O4   2–8–0

Built: 1911–20. Robinson GCR class 8K. Many also saw service on other railways in the first
world war, being ordered by the railway operating department. (ROD).
B.P.: 180 lb/sq. in.   **Weight –Loco:** 73.2 tons.   **Wheel dias.:** 3' 6", 4' 8".
Cyls.: 21" x 26" (O).   **–Tender:** 48.3 tons.   **T.E.:** 31 330 lbf.
Valve Gear: Stephenson.   **RA:** 6.

BR   LNER   GCR
63601*   5102–3509–3601   102   National Railway Museum   Gorton 1911
ROD
1984   Dorrigo, Northern New South Wales, Australia   NBL 22042/1918
2003   Dorrigo, Northern New South Wales, Australia   Gorton 1918
2004   Richmond Vale Steam Centre, Kurri-Kurri, NSW, Australia   Gorton 1918

CLASS J21   0–6–0

Built: 1886–95. Worsdell NER class C. 201 built.
B.P.: 160 lb/sq. in.   **Weight –Loco:** 43.75 tons.   **Wheel dia.:** 5' 1¼".
Cyls.: 19" x 24" (I).   **–Tender:** 36.95 tons.   **T.E.:** 19 240 lbf.
Valve Gear: Stephenson.   **RA:** 3.

BR   LNER   NER
65033   876–5033   876*   North of England Open Air Museum   Gateshead 1889

CLASS J36   0–6–0

Built: 1889–1900. Holmes NBR class C. 168 built.
B.P.: 165 lb/sq. in.   **Weight –Loco:** 41.95 tons.   **Wheel dia.:** 5' 0".
Cyls.: 18" x 26" (I).   **–Tender:** 33.5 tons.   **T.E.:** 20 240 lbf.
Valve Gear: Stephenson.   **RA:** 3.

BR   LNER   NBR
65243   9673–5243   673*★MAUDE   Bo'ness & Kinneil Railway   N 4392/1891

CLASS J15   0–6–0

Built: 1883–1913. Worsdell GER class Y14. 189 built.
B.P.: 160 lb/sq. in.   **Weight –Loco:** 37.1 tons.   **Wheel dia.:** 4' 11".
Cyls.: 17½" x 24" (I).   **–Tender:** 30.65 tons.   **T.E.:** 16 940 lbf.
Valve Gear: Stephenson.   **RA:** 1.   Dual brakes.

BR   LNER   GER
65462   7564*–5462   564   North Norfolk Railway   Stratford 1912

CLASS J17   0–6–0

Built: 1900–11. Holden GER class G58. 90 built (65500–89).
B.P.: 180 lb/sq. in.   **Weight –Loco:** 45.4 tons.   **Wheel dia.:** 4' 11".
Cyls.: 19" x 26" (I).   **–Tender:** 38.25 tons.   **T.E.:** 24 340 lbf.
Valve Gear: Stephenson.   **RA:** 4.   Air brakes.

BR   LNER   GER
65567   8217–5567   1217*   National Railway Museum   Stratford 1905

CLASS J27   0–6–0

Built: 1906–23. Worsdell NER class P3. 115 built.
B.P.: 180 lb/sq. in.   **Weight –Loco:** 47 tons.   **Wheel dia.:** 4' 7¼".
Cyls.: 18½" x 26" (I).   **–Tender:** 37.6 tons.   **T.E.:** 24 640 lbf.
Valve Gear: Stephenson.   **RA:** 5.

BR   *LNER*
65894   2392*–5894   North Yorkshire Moors Railway   Darlington 1923

CLASS J94   0–6–0ST

Built: 1943 for Ministry of Supply. 75 bought by LNER. Many sold to industrial users.
B.P.: 170 lb/sq. in.   **Wheel dia.:** 4′ 3″.   **T.E.:** 23 870 lbf.
Cyls.: 18″ x 26″ (I).   **Weight:** 48.25 tons.
Valve Gear: Stephenson.   **RA:** 5.

BR   *LNER*
68077*   8077   Keighley & Worth Valley Railway   AB 2215/1947
68078*   8078   Southall Railway Centre   AB 2212/1946

68077 is on loan to British Steel Scunthorpe. 68088 is under restoration at Hayes.

Note: There are six locomotives of this class preserved masquerading as ex-BR locos which were never in BR or LNER stock. These are:

"68005"–*Location unknown* (RSH 7169/1944).
"68006"–South Yorkshire Railway (HE 3888/195).
"68009"–Great Central Railway (on loan to B'ham Rly. Museum) (HE 3825/1953).
"68012"–Lavender Line, Isfield (HE 3193/1944).
"68072"–Colne Valley Railway (VF 5309/1945).
"68081"–Nene Valley Railway (HE 2855/1943).

CLASS Y5   0–4–0ST

Built: 1874–1903. Neilson & Co. design for GER (class 209). 8 built. Survivor sold in 1917.
B.P.: 140 lb/sq. in.   **Wheel dia.:** 3′ 7″.   **T.E.:** 7970 lbf.
Cyls.: 12″ x 20″ (O).   **Weight:** 21.2 tons.
Valve Gear: Stephenson.   **RA:** 1.

GER
229   North Woolwich Station Museum   N 2119/1876

CLASS Y7   0–4–0T

Built: 1888–1923. Worsdell NER class H. 24 built.
B.P.: 160 lb/sq. in.   **Wheel dia.:** 4′ 0″.   **T.E.:** 11 140 lbf.
Cyls.: 14″ x 20″ (I).   **Weight:** 22.7 tons.
Valve Gear: Joy.   **RA:** 1.
†No train brakes.

BR   *LNER*   *NER*
68088*† 985–8088   Great Central Railway   Darlington 1205/1923
     1310   1310*   Middleton Railway   Gateshead 38/1891

CLASS Y9   0–4–0ST

Built: 1882–99. Drummond NBR class G. 35 built.
B.P.: 130 lb/sq. in.   **Wheel dia.:** 3′ 8″.   **T.E.:** 9840 lbf.
Cyls.: 14″ x 20″ (I).   **Weight:** 27.8 tons.
Valve Gear: Stephenson.   **RA:** 2.

BR   *LNER*   *NBR*
68095   9042–8095   42*   Lytham Motive Power Museum   Cowlairs 1887

CLASS Y1   4wT

Built: 1925–33. Sentinel geared loco. 24 built.
B.P.: 275 lb/sq. in.   **Wheel dia.:** 2′ 6″.   **T.E.:** 7260 lbf.
Cyls.: 6¾″ x 9″ (I).   **Weight:** 19.8 tons.
Valve Gear: Rotary cam.   **RA:** 1.

BR   *LNER*
68153† 59–8153   Middleton Railway   S 8837/1933
† Also carried Departmental 54*.

CLASS J69   0–6–0T

Built: 1890–1904. holden GER class S56. 126 locos (including many rebuilt from J67).
B.P.: 180 lb/sq. in.   **Wheel dia.:** 4′ 0″.   **T.E.:** 19 090 lbf.

Cyls.: 16½" x 22" (I).
Valve Gear: Stephenson.

Weight: 42.45 tons.
RA: 3.

Air brakes.

BR	LNER	GER		
68633	7087–8633	87*	National Railway Museum	Stratford 1249/1904

CLASS J52   0–6–0ST

Built: 1897–1902. Ivatt GNR class J13. Many rebuilt from Stirling locos (built 1892–97).
B.P.: 170 lb/sq. in.
Cyls.: 18" x 26" (I).
Valve Gear: Stephenson.

Wheel dia.: 4' 8".
Weight: 51.7 tons.
RA: 5.

T.E.: 21 740 lbf.

BR	LNER	GNR		
68846	4247–8846	1247*	National Railway Museum	SS 4492/1899

CLASS J72   0–6–0T

Built: 1898–1925. Worsdell NER class E1. Further batch built 1949–51 by BR. 113 built.
B.P.: 140 lb/sq. in.
Cyls.: 17" x 24" (I).
Valve Gear: Stephenson.

Wheel dia.: 4' 1¼".
Weight: 38.6 tons.
RA: 5.

T.E.: 16 760 lbf.

69023*–Departmental No. 59	North Yorkshire Moors Railway	Darlington 2151/1951

This loco will be loaned to the South Devon Railway for the summer of 1991.

CLASS N2   0–6–2T

Built: 1920–29. Gresley GNR class N2. 107 built (69490–69596).
B.P.: 170 lb/sq. in.
Cyls.: 19" x 26" (I).
Valve Gear: Stephenson.

Wheel dia.: 5' 8", 3' 8".
Weight: 70.25 tons.
RA: 6.

T.E.: 19 950 lbf.

BR	LNER	GNR		
69523*	4744–9523	1744	Great Central Railway	NBL 22600/1921

CLASS N7   0–6–2T

Built: 1915–28. Hill GER class L77. 134 built (69600–69733).
B.P.: 180 lb/sq. in.
Cyls.: 18" x 24" (I).
Valve Gear: Walschaerts (inside).
Dual brakes.

Wheel dias.: 4' 10", 3' 9".
Weight: 61.8 tons.
RA: 5.

T.E.: 20 510 lbf.

BR	LNER	GER		
69621*	999E–7999–9621 999	"A.J. HILL" East Anglian Railway Museum	Stratford 1924

This loco will be loaned to the East Lancashire Railway for the summer of 1991.

CLASS X1   2–2–4T

Built: 1869 by NER as 2–2–2WT. Rebuilt 1892 to 4–2–2T and rebuilt as 2–cyl compound 2–2–4T and used for pulling inspections saloons. (NER class 66).
B.P.: 175 lb/sq. in.
Cyls.: 13" x 24" (hp) + 18½" x 20" (lp) (I).
Valve Gear: Stephenson.

Wheel dias.: 3' 7", 5' 7¾", 3' 1¼".

T.E.: 6390 lbf.
Weight: 44.95 tons.

LNER	NER		
66	1478*–66 AEROLITE	National Railway Museum	Gateshead 1869

NER 901 CLASS   2–4–0

Built: 1872–82. Fletcher design. 55 built.
B.P.: 160 lb/sq. in.
Cyls.: 18" x 24" (I).
Valve Gear: Stephenson.

Weight –Loco: 39.7 tons.
–Tender: 29.9 tons.

Wheel dias.: 4' 6", 7' 6".
T.E.: 12 590 lbf.

LNER	NER		
910	910*	Darlington North Road Museum (N)	Gateshead 1875

NER 1001 CLASS   0–6–0

Built: 1864–75. Bouch design for Stockton and Darlington Railway.
B.P.: 130 lb/sq. in.
Cyls.: 17" x 26" (I).
Valve Gear: Stephenson.

Weight –Loco: 35 tons.
–Tender: 18 tons.

Wheel dia.: 5' 0½".
T.E.: 13 720 lbf.

LNER	NER		
1275	1275*	National Railway Museum	Darlington 708/1874

CLASS E5   2–4–0

Built: 1885. Tennant NER 1463 class. 20 built.
B.P.: 160 lb/sq. in.   **Weight –Loco:** 42.1 tons.   **Wheel dias.:** 4' 6", 7' 0".
Cyls.: 18" x 24" (I).   **–Tender:** 32.1 tons.   **T.E.:** 12 590 lbf.
Valve Gear: Stephenson.

LNER	NER		
1463	1463*	Darlington North Road Museum (N)	Darlington 1885

CLASS D17   4–4–0

Built: 1893–7. Worsdell NER class M1 (later class M). 20 built.
B.P.: 160 lb/sq. in.   **Weight –Loco:** 52 tons.   **Wheel dias.:** 3' 7¼", 7' 1¼".
Cyls.: 19" x 26" (I).   **–Tender:** 41 tons.   **T.E.:** 14 970 lbf.
Valve Gear: Stephenson.   **RA:** 6.

LNER	NER		
1621	1621*	National Railway Museum	Gateshead 1893

CLASS C2   "KLONDYKE"   4–4–2

Built: 1898–1903. H. A. Ivatt GNR class C1. 22 built.
B.P.: 170 lb/sq. in.   **Weight –Loco:** 62 tons.   **Wheel dias.:** 3' 8", 6' 8", 3' 8".
Cyls.: 19" x 24" (O).   **–Tender:** 42.1 tons.   **T.E.:** 15 650 lbf.
Valve Gear: Stephenson.   **RA:** 4.

LNER	GNR			
3990	990*	HENRY OAKLEY	National Railway Museum	Doncaster 769/1898

GNR   4–2–2

Built: 1870–95. Stirling design.
B.P.: 140 lb/sq. in.   **Weight –Loco:** 38.5 tons.   **Wheel dias.:** 3' 10", 8' 1", 4' 1".
Cyls.: 18" x 28" (O).   **–Tender:** 30 tons.   **T.E.:** 11 130 lbf.
Valve Gear: Stephenson.

1		National Railway Museum	Doncaster 50/1870

STOCKTON & DARLINGTON RAILWAY   0–4–0

Built: 1825–6. G. Stephenson design. 6 built.
B.P.: 50 lb/sq. in.   **Weight –Loco:** 6.5 tons.   **Wheel dia.:** 3' 11".
Cyls.: 9½" x 24" (O).   **–Tender:**   **T.E.:** 2050 lbf.

1	LOCOMOTION	Darlington North Road Museum (N)	RS1/1825

STOCKTON & DARLINGTON RAILWAY   0–6–0

Built: 1845.
B.P.: 75 lb/sq. in.   **Weight –Loco:** 6.5 tons.   **Wheel dia.:** 4' 0".
Cyls.: 14½" x 24" (O).   **–Tender:** 0 tons.   **T.E.:** 6700 lbf.

25	DERWENT	Darlington North Road Museum (N)	Kitching 1845

ELECTRIC LOCOMOTIVES

CLASS EM1 (BR CLASS 76)   Bo+Bo

Built: 1941–53 at Doncaster (26000) and Gorton (others). 58 built. **System:** 1500 V dc.
Traction Motors: 4 MV 186 axle-hung.
Max Rail Power: 2460 kW (3300 hp).
Continuous Rating: 970 kW (1300 hp).
Max. T.E.: 200 kN (45000 lbf).   **Weight:** 88 tonnes.
Cont. T.E.: 39 kN (8800 lbf) at 56 mph.   **Wheel Dia:** 1270 mm.
Max. Speed: 65 mph.

26020*–E26020–76020	National Railway Museum	Gorton 1027/1951

CLASS ES1   NER   Bo–Bo

Built: 1905. 2 built. Used on Newcastle Riverside Branch. **System:** 600 V dc overhead.
Traction Motors: 4 BTH design.
Weight: **Wheel Dia:** 915 mm.

NER   LNER   BR

1*   4075–6480   26500   National Railway Museum   BE1905

CLASS EM2   Co–Co

Built: 1953–55 at Gorton. 7 built. Sold to Nederlandse Spoorwegen (NS)(Dutch Railways)
Traction Motors: 6 MV 146 axle-hung.
Max Rail Power: 1716 kW (2300 hp).
Max. T.E.: 200 kN (45000 lbf).   **Weight:** 102 tonnes.
Cont. T.E.: 78 kN (15600 lbf) at 23 mph.   **Wheel Dia:** 1092 mm.
Max. Speed: 90 mph.

NS   BR

1502	27000*–E 27000	ELECTRA	BR Ilford TMD	Gorton 1065/1953
1505*	27001–E 27001	ARIADNE	Gtr. Manchester Mus. of Sc. & Ind.	Gorton 1066/1954
1501*	27003–E 27003	(DIANA)	Rotterdam CS (NS)	Gorton 1068/1954

ELECTRIC MULTIPLE UNITS

NER   DMLV

Built: 1904. Driving motor luggage van for North Tyneside line. After withdrawal from capital stock, this vehicle was used as a rail de-icing car.
System: 675 V dc third rail.
Traction Motors:
DMLV   17.40 x 2.77 m   46 tons

BR   NER

DE 900730   3267   DMLV   North Tyneside Railway (N)   MCW 1904

CLASS 506   MANCHESTER–HADFIELD

Built: 1950 (Into service 1954).
System: 1500 V dc overhead.
Normal formation: DMBSO–TSO–DTSO.
Traction Motors: Four GEC 140 kW (187 hp).
Max. Speed: 70 mph.

DMBSO	18.41 x 2.82 m	51 tons	52S
TSO	16.78 x 2.82 m	26.5 tons	66S (originally TCO).
DTSO	16.87 x 2.82 m	28.5 tons	58S

M 59404 M	DMBSO	Midland Railway Centre	Metro-Cammell 1954
M 59504 M	TSO	Midland Railway Centre	Metro-Cammell 1954
M 59604 M	DTSO	Midland Railway Centre	BRCW 1954

GRIMSBY & IMMINGHAM LIGHT RAILWAY CARS

Built 1914 by GCR Dukinfield. Single Deck vehicle, 64 seats. **Type:** Single deck trams.
Seats: 48 (64*)(reduced to 44 on BR§).
Bogies: Brill (Brush*).
Motors: 2 x 25 hp Dick Kerr 31A (DK9*, 25A§) of 18 kW.

14*	National Tramway Museum, Crich	GCR Dukinfield 1914
20§	National Tramway Museum, Clay X	Gateshead & District Tramways Co. 1927 (No. 5.)
26	National Tramway Museum, Clay X	Gateshead & District Tramways Co. 1925 (No. 10)

BRITISH RAILWAYS STANDARD STEAM LOCOMOTIVES

GENERAL

From 1951 onwards BR produced a series of standard steam locomotives under the jurisdiction of R.A. Riddles. They were referred to by power classification. Tender engines were numbered in the 70000 series and tank engines in the 80000 series, the exceptions being the class 9F 2–10–0s which were numbered in the 92000 series.

CLASS 7P · BRITANNIA · 4–6–2

Built: 1951–54. 55 built.
B.P.: 250 lb/sq. in.
Cyls.: 20″ x 28″ (O).
Valve Gear: Walschaerts.
Weight –**Loco:** 94 tons.
–**Tender:** 49.15 tons.
RA: 7
Wheel dias.: 3′ 0″, 6′ 2″, 3′ 3½″.
T.E.: 32 160 lbf.
70000 has dual brakes.

| 70000★ | BRITANNIA | Steamtown, Carnforth | Crewe 1951 |
| 70013 | OLIVER CROMWELL | Bressingham Gardens (N) | Crewe 1951 |

CLASS 8P · 4–6–2

Built: 1954. 1 built.
B.P.: 250 lb/sq. in.
Cyls.: 18″ x 28″ (3).
Valve Gear: British Caprotti (outside).
Weight –**Loco:** 101.25 tons.
–**Tender:** 53.7 tons.
Wheel dias.: 3′ 0″, 6′ 2″, 3′ 3½″.
T.E.: 39 080 lbf.
RA: 8.

| 71000★ | DUKE OF GLOUCESTER | Didcot Railway Centre | Crewe 1954 |

CLASS 5MT · 4–6–0

Built: 1951–57. 172 built.
B.P.: 225 lb/sq. in.
Cyls.: 19″ x 28″ (O).
Valve Gear: Walschaerts. (§outside British Caprotti).
Weight –**Loco:** 76 tons.
–**Tender:** 49.15 tons.
Wheel dias.: 3′ 0″, 6′ 2″.
T.E.: 26 120 lbf.
RA: 5.
73050 has dual brakes.

73050	"CITY OF PETERBOROUGH"	Nene Valley Railway	Derby 1954
73082	CAMELOT	Bluebell Railway	Derby 1955
73096		Watercress Line	Derby 1955
73129§		Midland Railway Centre	Derby 1956
73156		East Lancashire Railway	Doncaster 1956

CLASS 4MT · 4–6–0

Built: 1951–57. 80 built.
B.P.: 225 lb/sq. in.
Cyls.: 18″ x 28″ (O).
Valve Gear: Walschaerts.
Weight –**Loco:** 67.9 tons.
–**Tender:** 42.15 tons.
RA: 4.
Wheel dias.: 3′ 0″, 5′ 8″.
T.E.: 25 520 lbf.

75014		North Yorkshire Moors Railway	Swindon 1951
75027		Bluebell Railway	Swindon 1954
75029	"THE GREEN KNIGHT"	East Somerset Railway	Swindon 1954
75069★		Severn Valley Railway	Swindon 1955
75078		Keighley & Worth Valley Railway	Swindon 1956
75079		Plym Valley Railway	Swindon 1956

CLASS 4MT   2-6-0

Built: 1952–57. 115 built.
B.P.: 225 lb/sq. in.
Cyls.: 17½" x 26" (O).
Valve Gear: Walschaerts.

Weight –Loco: 59.75 tons.   **Wheel dias.:** 3' 0", 5' 8".
–Tender: 42.15 tons.   **T.E.:** 24 170 lbf.
RA: 4.

76017	Watercress Line	Horwich 1953
76077	Gloucestershire–Warwickshire Railway	Horwich 1956
76079	East Lancashire Railway	Horwich 1957
76084	Diamond House, Church Street, South Leverton	Horwich 1957

CLASS 2MT   2-6-0

Built: 1952–56. 65 built.
B.P.: 200 lb/sq. in.
Cyls.: 16½" x 24" (O).
Valve Gear: Walschaerts.

Weight –Loco: 49.25 tons.   **Wheel dias.:** 3' 0", 5' 0".
–Tender: 36.85 tons.   **T.E.:** 18 510 lbf.
RA: 4.

78018	Darlington Railway Centre	Darlington 1954
78019	Severn Valley Railway	Darlington 1954
78022	Keighley & Worth Valley Railway	Darlington 1954

CLASS 4MT   2-6-4T

Built: 1951–57. 155 built.
B.P.: 225 lb/sq. in.
Cyls.: 18" x 28" (O).
Valve Gear: Walschaerts.

Wheel dias:. 3' 0", 5' 8".   **T.E.:** 25 520 lbf.
Weight: 86.65 tons.
RA: 4.

80002	Keighley & Worth Valley Railway	Derby 1952
80064	Bluebell Railway	Brighton 1953
80072	Swindon Railway Engineering	Brighton 1953
80078	Swanage Railway	Brighton 1954
80079	Severn Valley Railway	Brighton 1954
80080★	Midland Railway Centre	Brighton 1954
80097	East Lancashire Railway	Brighton 1954
80098	Midland Railway Centre	Brighton 1954
80100	Bluebell Railway	Brighton 1955
80104	Avon Valley Railway	Brighton 1955
80105	Bo'ness & Kinneil Railway	Brighton 1955
80135	North Yorkshire Moors Railway	Brighton 1956
80136	North Staffordshire Railway	Brighton 1956
80150	Butetown Historic Railway Society	Brighton 1956
80151	East Anglian Railway Museum	Brighton 1957

CLASS 2MT   2-6-2T

Built: 1956 as class 2MT 2–6–0 No. 78059. Under conversion to a class 2MT 2–6–2T.
B.P.: 200 lb/sq. in.   **Wheel dias:.** 3' 0", 5' 0".   **T.E.:** 18 510 lbf.
Cyls.: 16½" x 24" (O).   **Weight:** . tons.
Valve Gear: Walschaerts.   **RA:** 4.

84030	Bluebell Railway	Darlington 1956 reb. Bluebell

CLASS 9F   2-10-0

Built: 1954–60. 251 built. 92220 was the last steam loco to be built for BR.
B.P.: 250 lb/sq. in.   **Weight –Loco:** 86.7 tons.   **Wheel dias.:** 3' 0", 5' 0".
Cyls.: 20" x 28" (O).   **–Tender:** 52.5 tons.   **T.E.:** 39 670 lbf.
Valve Gear: Walschaerts.   **RA:** 4.

92134		Sail & Steam Engineering, Brightlingsea	Crewe 1956
92203	"BLACK PRINCE"	East Somerset Railway	Swindon 1959
92207	"MORNING STAR"	East Lancashire Railway	Swindon 1959
92212		Great Central Railway	Swindon 1959
92214		Midland Railway Centre	Swindon 1959
92219		Midland Railway Centre	Swindon 1960
92220★	EVENING STAR	National Railway Museum	Swindon 1960
92240		Bluebell Railway	Crewe 1958
92245		Butetown Historic Railway Society	Crewe 1958

WAR DEPARTMENT LOCOMOTIVES
GENERAL
Only main-line War Department locos plus those shunters which remained in War Department service after the war are shown in this section. The many WD shunters which spent most of their life in industrial service are not shown.

STEAM LOCOMOTIVES
CLASS WD   2–10–0
Built: 1943–45 by North British. 148 built.
B.P.: 225 lb/sq. in. **Weight –Loco**: 78.3 tons. **Wheel dias.**: ?, 4′ 8½″.
Cyls.: 19″ x 28″ (O). **–Tender**: 24.45 tons **T.E.**: 34 210 lbf.
Valve Gear: Walschaerts.
§ Hellenic Railways (Greece) Nos. 951 and 960 respectively.
† NS No. 5085*.

WD	Present			
600		GORDON	Severn Valley Railway	NBL 25437/1943
3652–73652§	601	"STURDEE"	Mid Hants Railway	NBL 25438/1943
3672*–73672§		"DAME VERA LYNN"	North Yorkshire Moors Railway	NBL 25458/1944
3755*–73755†		LONGMOOR	Utrecht Railway Museum, NL	NBL 25541/1945

CLASS WD   2–8–0
Built: 1943–45 by North British & Vulcan Foundry. 935 built.
B.P.: 225 lb/sq. in. **Weight –Loco**: 70.25 tons. **Wheel dias.**: ?, 4′ 8½″.
Cyls.: 19″ x 28″ (O). **–Tender**: 42.7 tons. **T.E.**: 34 210 lbf.
Valve Gear: Walschaerts.
This loco was purchased from the Swedish State Railways (SJ).

SJ	NS	SJ		
4464	1931*	5927–75927	Keighley & Worth Valley Railway	VF 5200/1945

To be restored to BR condition as "90733".

CLASS WD   0–6–0ST
For details see LNER Class J94.

WD	Present			
190			Colne Valley Railway	HE 3790/1952
191	23	"HOLMAN F. STEPHENS"	Kent & East Sussex Railway	HE 3791/1953
192	92	WAGGONER	Museum of Army Transport	HE 3792/1953
193		(SHROPSHIRE)	East Lancashire Railway	HE 3793/1953
194		"CUMBRIA"	Lakeside & Haverthwaite Railway	HE 3794/1953
196		ERROL LONSDALE	Watercress Line	HE 3796/1953
197	25	"NORTHIAM"	Kent & East Sussex Railway	HE 3797/1953
198	98	ROYAL ENGINEER	MoDAD, Long Marston	HE 3798/1953
200	24	"WILLIAM H. AUSTEN"	Kent & East Sussex Railway	HE 3800/1953

For other ex-WD steam locos see LMS class 8F.

DIESEL LOCOMOTIVE
LMS DESIGN   0–6–0DE
For details see LMS section (BR class 11).

NS	WD	Present		
508*	70269		Utrecht Railway Museum, Netherlands	Derby 1944
	70269	878-601	Lakeside & Haverthwaite Railway	Derby 1944

BR DIESEL & ELECTRIC LOCOMOTIVES
GENERAL
The steam locomotive reigned supreme for a very long time on the British railway network but there were tentative steps taken to find a more economical method of train operation during the 1930s, particularly on the LMS with diesel shunting locomotives, and several small building programmes were authorised. The second world war saw the transfer of a large proportion to War Department use, some of which were shipped across the Channel and were subsequently lost in action.

On the electric scene the North Eastern Railway built a small fleet of electric locomotives for hauling heavy coal and steel trains in Co. Durham.

From the mid-1950s the re-equipment of the railway network began in earnest and vast numbers of new, mainly diesel lcocmotives were constructed by British Railways and private contractors, many early examples of which are still in service.

NUMBERING SYSTEM
In the early days each railway company allocated locomotive numbers in accordance with its own policy. However, after nationalisation in 1948 a common system was devised and internal combustion locomotives were allocated five figure numbers in the series 10000–19999. Electric locomotives similarly were numbered in the 20000–29999 series.

In 1957 the locomotives were allocated new numbers to avoid duplication with steam locomotives, diesels being given a four-digit number prefixed with a 'D'. Diesel electric shunters in the 13xxx series had the '1' replaced by a 'D', but diesel mechanical shunters were completely renumbered. Electric locomotives were given an 'E' prefix.

When all steam locomotives had been withdrawn, the prefix letter was eliminated from the number of diesel locomotives.

With the introduction of modern communications each class was allocated a two digit class number followed by a three digit serial number.

CLASSIFICATION SYSTEM
It was not until the British Railways organisation was set up that some semblance of order was introduced. This broadly took the following form:

Type	Engine Horsepower	Number Range
1	800–1000	D 8000–D 8999
2	1001–1499	D 5000–D 6499
3	1500–1999	D 6500–D 7999
4	2000–2999	D 1–D 1999
5	3000 +	D 9000–D 9499
Shunting	150/300	D 2000–D 2999
Shunting	350/400	D 3000–D 4999
Shunting	650	D 9500–D 9999
AC Electric		E 1000–E 4999
DC Electric		E 5000–E 6999

Note: Locos & MU vehicles which have recently been preserved, but have not yet moved from BR are shown with the location left blank.

BR DIESEL & ELECTRIC LOCOMOTIVES
DIESEL LOCOMOTIVES
CLASS 44   PEAK   1Co–Co1
Built: 1959–60. 10 Built.
Engine: Sulzer 12LDA28A of 1720 kW (2300 hp) at 750 rpm.
Transmission: Electric. Six Crompton Parkinson C171B1 axle-hung traction motors.
Power at Rail: 1342 kW (1800 hp).

Max. T.E.: 245 kN (55000 lbf).
Cont. T.E.: 133 kN (30000 lbf) at 2000 mph.
Max. Speed: 90 mph.
Weight:135 tonnes.
Wheel Dias: 914/1143 mm.

| D 4*-44004 | GREAT GABLE | Midland Railway Centre | Derby 1959 |
| D 8*-44008 | PENYGHENT | Peak Railway Matlock | Derby 1959 |

CLASS 45   1Co–Co1

Built: 1960–63. 127 built.
Engine: Sulzer 12LDA28B of 1860 kW (2500 hp) at 750 rpm.
Transmission: Electric. Six Crompton Parkinson C172A1 axle-hung traction motors.
Power at Rail: 1491 kW (2000 hp).
Max. T.E.: 245 kN (55000 lbf).
Cont. T.E.: 133 kN (30000 lbf) at 90 mph.
Max. Speed: 90 mph.
Weight:138 tonnes.
Wheel Dias: 914/1143 mm.

D 22*-45132			Crewe 1961
D 40-45133*		Midland Railway Centre	Crewe 1961
D 61-45112*			Crewe 1961
D 67*-45118	THE ROYAL ARTILLERYMAN	Northampton Steam Railway	Crewe 1961
D 99-45135*	3rd CARABINIER	BR Tinsley TMD	Crewe 1961
D 100*-45060	SHERWOOD FORESTER	Peak Railway Matlock	Crewe 1961
D 120*-45108		Crewe Heritage Centre	Crewe 1961
D 123*-45125			Crewe 1961

CLASS 40   1Co–Co1

Built: 1958–62 at Vulcan Foundry & Robert Stephenson & Hawthorn. 200 built.
Engine: English Electric 16SVT MkII of 1480 kW (2000 hp) at 850 rpm.
Transmission: Electric. Six EE 526/5D axle-hung traction motors.
Power at Rail: 1156 kW (1550 hp).
Max. T.E.: 231 kN (52000 lbf).
Cont. T.E.: 137 kN (30900 lbf) at 18.8 mph.
Max. Speed: 90 mph.
Weight: 132 tonnes.
Wheel Dias: 914/1143 mm.

D 200*-40122		National Railway Museum	EE/VF 2367/D395 1958
D 212-40012*-97407	AUREOL	Midland Railway Centre	EE/VF 2667/D429 1959
D 213-40013*	ANDANIA	South Yorkshire Railway	EE/VF 2668/D430 1959
D 306*-40106	"ATLANTIC CONVEYOR"	Nene Valley Railway	EE/RSH 2726/8136 1960
D 318-40118*-97408		Birmingham Railway Mus.	EE/RSH 2853/8148 1961
D 335*-40135-97406		East Lancashire Railway	EE/VF 3081/D631 1961
D 345-40145*		East Lancashire Railway	EE/VF 3091/D641 1961

CLASS 50   Co–Co

Built: 1967–68 at Vulcan Foundry. 50 built.
Engine: English Electric 16CVST of 2010 kW (2700 hp) at 850 rpm.
Transmission: Electric. Six EE 538/5A axle-hung traction motors.
Power at Rail: 1540 kW (2070 hp).
Max. T.E.: 216 kN (48500 lbf).
Cont. T.E.: 147 kN (33000 lbf) at 18.8 mph.
Max. Speed: 100 mph.
Weight: 117 tonnes.
Wheel Dia: 1092 mm.

| D 419-50019* | RAMILLIES | EE/VF 3789/D1160 1968 |
| D 435-50035* | ARK ROYAL | EE/VF 3805/D1176 1968 |

CLASS 42   WARSHIP   B–B

Built: 1958–61. 38 Built.
Engines: Two Maybach MD650 of 1642 kW (2200 hp) at 1530 rpm.
Transmission: Hydraulic. Mekydro K 104U.
Power at Rail:
Max. T.E.: 223 kN (52400 lbf).
Cont. T.E.: 209 kN (46900 lbf) at 11.5 mph.
Max. Speed: 90 mph.
Weight: 80 tonnes.
Wheel Dia: 1033 mm.

| D 821 | GREYHOUND | North Yorkshire Moors Railway | Swindon 1960 |
| D 832 | ONSLAUGHT | East Lancashire Railway | Swindon 1961 |

CLASS 52   WESTERN   C–C

Built: 1961–64. 74 built.
Engines: Two Maybach MD655 of 1007 kW (1350 hp) at 1500 rpm.
Transmission: Hydraulic. Voith L630rV.
Power at Rail:
Max. T.E.: 297.3 kN (66770 lbf).   **Weight:** 111 tonnes.
Cont. T.E.: 201.2 kN (45200 lbf) at 14.5 mph.   **Wheel Dia:** 1092 mm.
Max. Speed: 90 mph.

D 1010§	WESTERN CAMPAIGNER	West Somerset Railway	Swindon 1962
D 1013	WESTERN RANGER	Severn Valley Railway	Swindon 1962
D 1015	WESTERN CHAMPION	BR Old Oak Common CARMD	Swindon 1963
D 1023	WESTERN FUSILIER	National Railway Museum	Swindon 1963
D 1041	WESTERN PRINCE	East Lancashire Railway	Crewe 1962
D 1048	WESTERN LADY	Bodmin Steam Railway	Crewe 1962
D 1062	WESTERN COURIER	Severn Valley Railway	Crewe 1963

§ Masquerades as D 1035 WESTERN YEOMAN.

CLASS 47   Co–Co

Built: 1963–67. 512 built.
Engine: Sulzer 12LDA28C of 1920 kW (2580 hp) at 750 rpm.
Transmission: Electric. Six Brush TG 160-60 axle-hung traction motors.
Power at Rail: 1550 kW (2080 hp).
Max. T.E.: 267 kN (60000 lbf).   **Weight:** 112 tonnes.
Cont. T.E.: 133 kN (33000 lbf) at 26 mph.   **Wheel Dias:** 1143 mm.
Max. Speed: 95 mph.

D 1842*-47192	Crewe Heritage Centre	Crewe 1965

CLASS 03   0–6–0

Built: 1957–62. 230 built.
Engine: Gardner 8L3 of 152 kW (204 hp) at 1200 rpm.
Transmission: Mechanical. Wilson CA5 epicyclic gearbox.
Max. T.E.: 68 kN (15300 lbf).   **Weight:** 31 tonnes.
Wheel Dia: 1092 mm.   **Max. Speed:** 28 mph.

BR	Present		
11197-D 2010-03010		Trieste, Italy	Swindon 1958
11199-D 2012-03012*		Mayer-Parry, Snailwell (OOU)	Swindon 1958
11205-D 2018-03018*	No. 2/600	Ferrous Fragmentisers, Willesden	Swindon 1958
11206-D 2019		Brescia, Italy	Swindon 1958
11207-D 2020-03020*		Mayer-Parry, Snailwell	Swindon 1958
11209-D 2022*-03022		Swindon & Cricklade Railway	Swindon 1958
11210-D 2023	46	Kent & East Sussex Railway	Swindon 1958
11211-D 2024	47	Kent & East Sussex Railway	Swindon 1958
D 2027-03027	18	South Yorkshire Railway	Swindon 1958
D 2032		Brescia, Italy	Swindon 1958
D 2033		Brescia, Italy	Swindon 1958
D 2036		Brescia, Italy	Swindon 1959
D 2037-03037*		BCOE Oxcroft DP	Swindon 1959
D 2041		Colne Valley Railway	Swindon 1959
D 2046	Unnumbered	Gulf Oil Co., Waterston	Doncaster 1958
D 2051	4	Ford Motor Co., Dagenham	Doncaster 1959
D 2059*-03059		Isle of Wight Steam Railway	Doncaster 1959
D 2062-03062*		Dean Forest Railway	Doncaster 1959
D 2063-03063*		Colne Valley Railway	Doncaster 1959
D 2066-03066*		South Yorkshire Railway	Doncaster 1959
D 2069-03069*		Vic Berry Leicester	Doncaster 1959
D 2070		South Yorkshire Railway	Doncaster 1959
D 2072-03072*		Lakeside & Haverthwaite Railway	Doncaster 1959
D 2073-03073*		Crewe Heritage Centre	Doncaster 1959
D 2078-03078*		North Tyneside Railway	Doncaster 1959
D 2081-03081	661	Stoomcentrum, Maldegem, Belgium	Doncaster 1960
D 2089-03089*		British Sugar, Peterborough	Doncaster 1960
D 2090-03090*		National Railway Museum	Doncaster 1960
D 2094-03094*		South Yorkshire Railway	Doncaster 1960

BR	Present	Location	Works
D 2099-03099	Unnumbered	NSF Monkton Coking Plant (OOU)	Doncaster 1960
D 2112-03112*		British Sugar, Peterborough	Doncaster 1960
D 2113-03113	Unnumbered	Gulf Oil Co., Waterston (OOU)	Doncaster 1960
D 2117	LHR No. 8	Lakeside & Haverthwaite Railway	Swindon 1959
D 2118	Unnumbered	Costain Dowmac, Lenwade	Swindon 1959
D 2119-03119*	LINDA	Dean Forest Railway	Swindon 1959
D 2120-03120*		W.H. McAlpine, Fawley Hill	Swindon 1959
D 2128-03128		Stoomcentrum, Maldegem, Belgium	Swindon 1960
D 2133*		British Cellophane Bridgwater	Swindon 1960
D 2138*		Midland Railway Centre	Swindon 1960
D 2139	No. 1	NSF Monkton Coking Plant	Swindon 1960
D 2144*-03144	WESTERN WAGGONER	MoDAD, Long Marston	Swindon 1961
D 2148		Steamport Railway Museum	Swindon 1960
D 2150	Unnumbered	British Salt, Middlewich	Swindon 1960
D 2152*-03152		Swindon Railway Engineering	Swindon 1960
D 2153-03153	?	Trieste, Italy	Swindon 1960
D 2156-03156	?	Trieste, Italy	Swindon 1960
D 2157-03157	?	Trieste, Italy	Swindon 1960
D 2162-03162*		Llangollen Railway	Swindon 1960
D 2164-03164	?	Trieste Italy	Swindon 1960
D 2170-03170*		Otis Euro Trans-Rail, Salford	Swindon 1960
D 2178		Caerphilly Railway Society	Swindon 1962
D 2180-03180*		Mayer-Parry, Snailwell	Swindon 1962
D 2182		Victoria Park, Leamington Spa	Swindon 1962
D 2184		Colne Valley Railway	Swindon 1962
D 2192	ARDENT	South Devon Railway	Swindon 1961
D 2196-03196	40 JOYCE	Steamtown, Carnforth	Swindon 1961
D 2199		South Yorkshire Railway	Swindon 1961
Dept 92-D 2371-03371*		Rowden Mill Station, Herefordshire	Swindon 1958
D 2381		Steamtown Carnforth	Swindon 1961
D 2399-03399*		Mangapps Farm, Burnham-on-Crouch	Doncaster 1961

CLASS 04   0–6–0

Built: 1952–62. Drewry design built by Vulcan Foundry & Robert Stephenson & Hawthorn. 140 built.
Engine: Gardner 8L3 of 152 kW (204 hp) at 1200 rpm.
Transmission: Mechanical. Wilson CA5 epicyclic gearbox
Max. T.E.: 69.7 kN (15650 lbf).   **Weight:** 32 tonnes.
Wheel Dia: 1067 mm.   **Max. Speed:** 28 mph.

BR	Present	Location	Works
11103-D 2203*		Embsay Steam Railway	DC/VF 2400/D145/1952
11106-D 2205*		West Somerset Railway	DC/VF 2486/D212/1953
11108-D 2207*		North Yorkshire Moors Railway	DC/VF 2482/D208/1953
11117-D 2216		Brescia, Italy	DC/VF 2539/D265/1955
11135-D 2229*		South Yorkshire Railway	DC/VF 2552/D278/1955
11151-D 2232		Rome, Italy	DC/VF 2556/D282/1956
11215-D 2245		Battlefield Steam Railway	DC/RSH 2577/7864/1956
11216-D 2246	BLUEBELL	Coal Mechanisation Tolworth	DC/RSH 2578/7865/1956
D 2267	1	Ford Motor Co. Dagenham	DC/RSH 2611/7897/1958
D 2271	2271	West Somerset Railway	DC/RSH 2615/7901/1958
D 2272	ALFIE	British Fuels Blackburn CCD	DC/RSH 2616/7902/1958
D 2279		East Anglian Railway Museum	DC/RSH 2656/8097/1960
D 2280	No. 2	Ford Motor Co. Dagenham	DC/RSH 2657/8098/1960
D 2284		South Yorkshire Railway	DC/RSH 2661/8102/1960
D 2289		Brescia, Italy	DC/RSH 2669/8122/1960
D 2295		Brescia, Italy	DC/RSH 2675/8128/1960
D 2298	LORD WENLOCK	Buckinghamshire Railway Centre	DC/RSH 2679/8151/1960
D 2302		Papworths Ely	DC/RSH 2683/8161/1960
D 2310		Coal Mechanisation, Tolworth	DC/RSH 2691/8160/1960
D 2324	Unnumbered	Location Unknown	DC/RSH 2705/8183/1961
D 2325		Mangapps Farm, Burnham-on-Crouch	DC/ RSH 2706/8184/1961
D 2333	3	Ford Motor Co. Dagenham (OOU)	DC/RSH 2714/8192/1961
D 2334		South Yorkshire Railway	DC/RSH 2715/8193/1961
D 2337		South Yorkshire Railway	DC/RSH 2718/8196/1961

CLASS 06   0–4–0

Built: 1958–60 by Andrew Barclay, Kilmarnock. 35 built.
Engine: Gardner 8L3 of 152 kW (204 hp) at 1200 rpm.
Transmission: Mechanical. Wilson CA5 epicyclic gearbox.
Max. T.E.: 88 kN (19800 lbf).   **Weight:** 37 tonnes.
Wheel Dia: 1092 mm.   **Max. Speed:** 23 mph.

D 2420–06003*–97804   South Yorkshire Railway   AB 435/1959

UNCLASSIFIED   HUDSWELL-CLARKE   0–6–0

Built: 1955–61. 20 built.
Engine: Gardner 8L3 of 152 kW (204 hp) at 1200 rpm.
Transmission: Mechanical. SSS powerflow double synchro.
Max. T.E.: 85.7 kN (19245 lbf).   **Weight:** 34 tonnes.
Cont. T.E.: 76 kN (17069 lbf) at 3.72 mph. **Wheel Dia:** 1067 mm.
Max. Speed: 25 mph.

D 2511   Keighley & Worth Valley Railway   HC D1202/1961

CLASS 05   0–6–0

Built: 1955–61. 69 built.
Engine: Gardner 8L3 of 152 kW (204 hp) at 1200 rpm.
Transmission: Mechanical. Hunslet gearbox.
Max. T.E.: 64.6 kN (14500 lbf).   **Weight:** 31 tonnes.
Wheel Dia: 1016 mm.   **Max. Speed:** 18 mph.

BR	Present		
11140-D 2554*-05001			
-97803		Isle of Wight Steam Railway	HE 4870/1956
D 2578	2 "CIDER QUEEN"	Bulmers Railway Centre	HE 5460/1958
			rebuilt HE 6999/1968
D 2587		East Lancashire Railway	HE 5636/1959
			rebuilt HE 7180/1969
D 2595		Steamport Railway Museum	HE 5642/1959
			rebuilt HE 7179/1969

UNCLASSIFIED   NORTH BRITISH   0–4–0

Built: 1957–61. 73 built.
Engine: M.A.N. W6V 17.5/22A of 168 kW (225 hp) at 1100 rpm.
Transmission: Mechanical. Voith L33YU.
Max. T.E.: 89.4 kN (20080 lbf).   **Weight:** 28 tonnes.
Cont. T.E.: 53.4 kN (12000 lbf) at 4 mph. **Wheel Dia:** 1067 mm.
Max. Speed: 15 mph.

D 2767   East Lancashire Railway   NBL 28020/1960
D 2774   East Lancashire Railway   NBL 28027/1960

CLASS 02   0–4–0

Built: 1960–61. 20 built.
Engine: Rolls Royce C6NFL of 127 kW (170 hp) at 1800 rpm.
Transmission: Hydraulic. Rolls Royce CF 10000.
Max. T.E.: 66.8 kN (15000 lbf).   **Weight:** 28.6 tonnes.
Cont. T.E.: 61 kN (13700 lbf) at 1.4 mph. **Wheel Dia:** 1067 mm.
Max. Speed: 30 mph.

BR	Present		
D 2853-02003*	PETER	L.C.P. Fuels, Shutt End, Brierley Hill	YE 2812/1960
D 2854		South Yorkshire Railway	YE 2813/1960
D 2857	Unnumbered	Birds Comml. Metals Long Marston	YE 2816/1960
D 2858	Unnumbered	Butterley Co. Ltd, Ripley	YE 2817/1960
D 2860		National Railway Museum	YE 2843/1961
D 2866		Caledonian Railway	YE 2849/1961
D 2867	DIANNE	Redland Aggregates, Barrow-on-Soar	YE 2850/1961
D 2868	SAM	L.C.P. Fuels, Shutt End, Brierley Hill	YE 2851/1961

Ex-LNER Class A4 4-6-2 No. 60009 is seen backing into Foley Park Tunnel on the Severn Valley Railway whilst preparing for a run-past for Central TV. This locomotive at present carries the name "OSPREY", a name allocated to it but never previously carried. Its correct name is UNION OF SOUTH AFRICA.

Bryan Hicks

▲LNER Class V2 2–6–2 No. 4771 GREEN ARROW speeds south out of Lazonby Tunnel on the Settle Jn.–Carlisle line with a southbound special on 30th September 1989. *Hugh Ballantyne*

▼LNER Sentinel Class Y1 Departmental No. 54 on the Middleton Railway, Leeds on 15th July 1989. *Hugh Ballantyne*

GCR 'Improved Director' (LNER Class D11) 4–4–0 No. 506 BUTLER HENDERSON near Swithland Resevoir on the Great Central Railway with the 13.00 'Carillon' restaurant car train from Loughborough to Rothley on 5th August 1990.
David Marriott

LNER Class A3 4–6–2 No. 4472 FLYING SCOTSMAN is seen at Sunnyhill on the outskirts of Derby with a return Derby–Didcot charter on 15th September 1990.
Chris Milner

LNER Class K4 2–6–2 No. 3442 THE GREAT MARQUESS is seen leaving Bridgnorth on the Severn Valley Railway with the 17.05 goods to Kidderminster.

Hugh Ballantyne

▲Ex-GER Class N7 0–6–2T No. 69621 is a recent addition to the ranks of steam locomotives authorised to run on BR. It is seen at Cambridge on a 'West Anglia Open Day' on 30th September 1989. It has since been named "A.J. HILL". *E.H. Sawford*

▼GNR 4–2–2 No. 1 was photographed in the National Railway Museum, York, before removal for so-called improvements to the building. *E.H. Sawford*

▲NER 4–4–0 No. 1621 on display in the Peter Allen Building at the NRM, York.   *E.H. Sawford*
▼BR standard Class 9F 2–10–0 No. 92240 stands inside the new extension to the workshop at Sheffield Park, Bluebell Railway on 11th April 1990 whilst a major rebuild was taking place.
Colin Marsden

▲Standard Class 4MT 2–6–4T No. 80080 is seen on a demonstration train at the Coalville Freight Centre open day on 11th June 1989.   *C.J. Tuffs*

▼War Department 2–10–0 No. 600 GORDON nears Bewdley Tunnel on the Severn Valley Railway with a Santa special from Arley to Kidderminster on 9th December 1990.   *Hugh Ballantyne*

Class 25 Bo-Bo No. D 7633 approaches Bewdley (SVR) with the 15.23 to Kidderminster on 14th October 1990.

Tom Clift

The two Class 40s owned by the Class 40 preservation society Nos. D 335 and 40145 double-head the 15.30 Ramsbottom–Bury service on the East Lancashire Railway on 7th October 1990.

Robin Trinder

▲The Midland Railway Centre's diesel and steam weekend with the newest arrival on the line, Class 45/1 No. 45133 departing Butterley with the 12.40 to Ironville on 19th August 1990.
Philip Crumpton

▼One of the attractions on the Nene Valley Railway during its first diesel weekend was the use of 'Western' diesel-hydraulic D 1013 WESTERN RANGER. It is seen here with a rake of Danish Coaches near Castor with a Wansford–Peterborough service on 6th October 1990. *Martin Loader*

▲Beyer-Peacock 'Hymek' diesel-hydraulic No. D 7076 nears Bewdley (SVR) on 19th May 1990 with the 16.18 Kidderminster–Bridgnorth. *C.J. Tuffs*

▼A pair of Deltics Nos. D 9000 ROYAL SCOTS GREY and D 9016 GORDON HIGHLANDER on display at Gloucester Rail Day on 1st July 1990. *Chris Milner*

Class 14 0–6–0 diesel-hydraulic No. D 9537 passes the site of Hayles Abbey Halt on the Gloucestershire–Warwickshire Railway with the 16.00 Toddington–Gretton on 8th July 1990.
Hugh Ballantyne

▲Class 27 No. D 5410 is seen arriving at Hampton Loade station (SVR) with the 11.28 Kidderminster–Bridgnorth service on 19th May 1990. *C.J. Tuffs*

▼Class 55 'Deltic' Co–Co No. 55015 TULYAR is seen departing from Swanwick Junction (Midland Railway Centre) on 16th September 1990. *John Eggleshaw*

▲Reputed to be the oldest production diesel locomotive to be recoverd for preservation, ex-LMS No. 7069 carrying the identification of the "Mammers Saint Calais" railway stands awaiting restoration at Swanage Station on 3rd April 1988. *Mervyn Turvey*

▼Another old LMS diesel shunter is No. 7401 built by Hunslet in 1932. This was photographed at the 30th anniversary celebrations of the Middleton railway during 1990. *Mervyn Turvey*

▲GWR diesel railcar No. 22 on display at Bescot open day on 6th May 1990. *Hugh Ballantyne*

▼Class 126 Inter-City DMU cars Nos 51017 and 59404 under restoration at Brechin on the Caledonian Railway on 28th May 1990. *Les Nixon*

▲An unusual visitor to Swindon Workshops was NER No. 1 Bo–Bo electric (LNER Class ES1). It is seen as part of the 'NRM on tour' exhibition on 1st July 1990. On the same track can be seen Class 76 No. 26020. *Mervyn Turvey*

▼Class 105 (Cravens) 2-car DMU E 51485/E 56121 resides on the West Somerset Railway at Minehead. *Brian Cuttel*

CLASS 01

0–4–0

Built: 1956. 4 built.
Engine: Gardner 6L3 of 114 kW (153 hp) at 1200 rpm.
Transmission: Mechanical. Wilson SE4 epicyclic
Max. T.E.: 56.8 kN (12750 lbf).   **Weight:** 25.5 tonnes.
Wheel Dia: 965 mm.
Max. Speed: 14 mph.

BR	Present		
11503-D 2953*		South Yorkshire Railway	AB 395/1955
11506-D 2956*	01003	East Lancashire Railway	AB 398/1956

CLASS 07

0–6–0

Built: 1962. 14 built.
Engine: Paxman 6RPHL Mk III of 205 kW (275 hp) at 1360 rpm.
Transmission: Electric. One AEI RTB 6652 traction motor.
Power at Rail: 142 kW (190 hp).
Max. T.E.: 126 kN (28240 lbf).   **Weight:** 43.6 tonnes.
Cont. T.E.: 71 kN (15950 lbf) at 4.38 mph.   **Wheel Dia:** 1067 mm.
Max. Speed: 20 mph.

BR	Present		
D 2985-07001*	Unnumbered	South Yorkshire Railway	RH 480686/1962
D 2989-07005*	"LANGBAURGH"	ICI Wilton Works, Middlesbrough (OOU)	RH 480690/1962
D 2994*-07010		West Somerset Railway	RH 480695/1962
D 2995-07011*	"CLEVELAND"	ICI Wilton Works, Middlesbrough	RH 480696/1962
D 2996-07012*		PD Fuels, Coed Bach DP	RH 480697/1962
D 2997-07013	Unnumbered	Dow Chemicals, Kings Lynn	RH 480698/1962

CLASS 08

0–6–0

Built: 1952–62. Built at Derby, Darlington, Crewe, Horwich & Doncaster. 996 built.
Engine: English Electric 6KT of 298 kW (400 hp) at 680 rpm.
Transmission: Electric. Two EE 506 axle-hung traction motors.
Power at Rail: 194 kW (260 hp).
Max. T.E.: 156 kN (35000 lbf).   **Weight:** 50 tonnes.
Cont. T.E.: 49.4 kN (11100 lbf) at 8.8 mph.   **Wheel Dia:** 1372 mm.
Max. Speed: 15 mph.

BR	Present		
13000-D 3000*		Brighton Locomotive Works	Derby 1952
13002-D 3002*		Plym Valley Railway	Derby 1952
13003-D 3003	22	Wanstrow Childrens Playground	Derby 1952
13014-D 3014	3014	Paignton & Dartmouth Railway	Derby 1952
13019-D 3019-3019*		PD Fuels, Gwaun-Cae-Gurwen DP	Derby 1953
13022-D 3022*-08015		Severn Valley Railway	Derby 1953
13023-D 3023-08016*	Unnumbered	Hargreaves, British Oak DP	Derby 1953
13029*-D 3029-08021		Birmingham Railway Museum	Derby 1953
13030-D 3030-08022	LION	Arthur Guinness, Park Royal London	Derby 1953
13044-D 3044-08032	33 "MENDIP"	Foster Yeoman, Merehead	Derby 1954
13047-D 3047	?	Lamco Mining Co., Liberia	Derby 1954
13059-D 3059*-08046	"Brechin City"	Caledonian Railway	Derby 1954
13067-D 3067-08054	210277	Tilcon Grassington	Derby 1954
13074-D 3074-08060	"UNICORN"	Arthur Guinness, Park Royal, London	Darlington 1953
13079-D 3079-08064*		National Railway Museum	Darlington 1953
13092-D 3092	?	Lamco Mining Co., Liberia	Darlington 1954
13094-D 3094	?	Lamco Mining Co., Liberia	Derby 1954
13098-D 3098	?	Lamco Mining Co., Liberia	Derby 1954
13100-D 3100	?	Lamco Mining Co., Liberia	Derby 1955
13101-D 3101*		Great Central Railway	Derby 1955
13102-D 3102-08077	Unnumbered	Wiggins Teape, Fort William	Derby 1955
13110-D 3110-08085*		RFS, Doncaster	Derby 1955
13167-D 3167*-08102		Lincoln Station	Derby 1955
13174-D 3174-08108*		Dower Wood, Newmarket Grain Terminal	Derby 1955
13179-D 3179-08113*		PD Fuels, Gwaun-Cae-Gurwen DP	Derby 1955
13180-D 3180-08114*		Great Central Railway	Derby 1955
13183-D 3183*		location unknown	Derby 1955

13190-D 3190-08123*	"George Mason"	Cholsey & Wallingford Railway	Derby	1955
13201-D 3201-08133*		Sheerness Steel Co.	Derby	1955
13225-D 3225-08157	1020	Independant Sea Terminals, Ridham Dock	Darlington	1955
13232-D 3232-08164	002 "PRUDENCE"	RFS Industries, Doncaster	Darlington	1956
13236-D 3236*-08168		BREL, York Works	Darlington	1956
13238-D 3238-08170*		RFS, Kilnhurst	Darlington	1956
13245-D 3245*-08177		BREL, Crewe Works	Derby	1956
13255-D 3255	3255	Brighton Locomotive Works	Derby	1956
13261-D 3261	?	Brighton Locomotive Works	Derby	1956
13265-D 3265*-08195	"MARK"	Llangollen Railway	Derby	1955
13272-D 3272-08202*		Papworth's, Ely	Derby	1955
13286-D 3286-08216*		Sheerness Steel Co.	Derby	1956
13290-D 3360-08220*		Steamtown, Carnforth	Derby	1956
13308-D 3308-08238	Unnumbered	Swindon Railway Engineering	Darlington	1956
13336-D 3336*-08266		Keighley & Worth Valley Railway	Darlington	1957
D 3358*-08288		Watercress Line	Derby	1957
D 3362-08292*		Deanside Transit, Hillington, Glasgow	Derby	1957
D 3366*-08296		BREL, Crewe Works	Derby	1957
D 3390-08320	P400D	English China Clay Ports, Fowey	Derby	1957
D 3401-08331	001 "TERENCE"	RFS Industries, Doncaster	Derby	1958
D 3415-08345*		Deanside Transit, Hillington Glasgow	Derby	1958
D 3420*-08350		North Staffordshire Railway	Crewe	1957
D 3429*-08359		Peak Railway, Darley Dale	Crewe	1958
D 3462-08377*		Dean Forest Railway	Darlington	1957
D 3513-08398	Unnumbered	English China Clay Ports, Methrose	Derby	1958
D 3538-08423	Unnumbered	Trafford Park Estates, Manchester	Derby	1958
D 3558-08443*		Scottish Grain Distillers, Cambus, Alloa	Derby	1958
D 3559-08444*		Bodmin Steam Railway	Derby	1958
D 3585-08470*		BREL, Crewe	Crewe	1958
D 3586*-08471		Severn Valley Railway	Crewe	1958
D 3591*-08476		Swanage Railway	Crewe	1958
D 3605-08490*		Strathspey Railway	Horwich	1958
D 3657-08502*		ICI Wilton Works, Middlesbrough	Doncaster	1958
D 3658-08503*		ICI Wilton Works, Middlesbrough	Doncaster	1958
D 3763-08596*		Bowaters (UK) Paper Co., Sittingbourne	Derby	1959
D 3765-08598*		PD Fuels, Gwaun-Cae-Gurwen DP	Derby	1959
D 3769-08602	"CLARENCE"	RFS Industries, Doncaster	Derby	1959
D 3817-08650*		Foster-Yeoman, Merehead	Horwich	1959
D 3836-08669*		Trafford Park Estates, Manchester	Horwich	1959
D 3845-08678*	"678 ULVERSTONIAN"	Glaxochem, Plumpton Junction	Horwich	1959
D 3871-08704*		Port of Boston Ltd.	Horwich	1960
D 3896-08728*		Deanside Transit, Hillington, Glasgow	Crewe	1960
D 3904-08736*		Deanside Transit, Hillington, Glasgow	Crewe	1960
D 3932-08764	"FLORENCE"	RFS Industries, Doncaster	Horwich	1961
D 3937-08769		Fire Service Training Centre, Moreton-in-Marsh	Derby	1960
D 3942-08774	"ARTHUR VERNON DAWSON"	A.V. Dawson, Middlesbrough	Derby	1960
D 3984-08816	Unnumbered	Cobra, Middlesbrough	Derby	1960
D 4014-08846		BREL, Derby Carriage Works	Horwich	1961
D 4039-08871		Humberside Sea & Land Services, Grimsby	Horwich	1961

13102 & 13201 are being overhauled by RFS, Kilnhurst.
08602 is on hire to Bowater's, Sittingbourne, whilst 08596 is under repair at RFS, Kilnhurst.
08764 is on hire to BREL Ltd., Derby Carriage Works.

CLASS 10   0–6–0

Built: 1955–62. Built at Darlington & Doncaster. 146 built.
Engine: Lister Blackstone ER6T of 261 kW (350 hp) at 750 rpm.
Transmission: Electric. Two GEC WT 821 axle-hung traction motors.
Power at Rail: 198 kW (265 hp).
Max. T.E.: 156 kN (35000 lbf).   **Weight**: tonnes.
Cont. T.E.: 53.4 kN (12000 lbf) at 8.2 mph.   **Wheel Dia**: 1372 mm.
Max. Speed: 20 mph.

BR	*Present*			
D 3452		Bodmin Steam Railway	Darlington	1957
D 3476		South Yorkshire Railway	Darlington	1957

D 3489*	"COLONEL TOMLINE"	Felixstowe Dock & Railway Co	Darlington 1958
D 3639	?	Conakry, Guinea, West Africa	Darlington 1958
D 3649	?	Conakry, Guinea, West Africa	Darlington 1958
D 4067	†	Great Central Railway	Darlington 1961
D 4092*	"CHRISTINE"	South Yorkshire Railway	Darlington 1962

† "MARGARET ETHEL-THOMAS ALFRED NAYLOR".

CLASS 24   Bo–Bo

Built: 1958–61 at Derby, Crewe & Darlington. 151 built.
Engine: Sulzer 6LDA28A of 870 kW (1160 hp) at 750 rpm.
Transmission: Electric. Four BTH 137BY axle-hung traction motors.
Power at Rail: 629 kW (843 hp).
Max. T.E.: 178 kN (40000 lbf).   **Weight:** 78 (81§) tonnes.
Cont. T.E.: 95 kN (21300 lbf) at 4.38 mph.   **Wheel Dia:** 1143 mm.
Max. Speed: 75 mph.

D 5032*§-24032 "HELEN TURNER"	North Yorkshire Moors Railway	Crewe 1959
D 5054*-24054-ADB 968008	East Lancashire Railway	Crewe 1959
D 5081-24081*	Steamport Railway Museum	Crewe 1960

CLASS 25   Bo–Bo

Built: 1961–67. Built at Darlington, Derby & Beyer Peacock. 327 built.
Engine: Sulzer 6LDA28D of 930 kW (1250 hp) at 750 rpm.
Transmission: Electric. Four AEI 253AY axle-hung traction motors.
Power at Rail: 708 kW (949 hp).
Max. T.E.: 200 kN (45000 lbf).   **Weight:** 72 (76§) tonnes.
Cont. T.E.: 93 kN (20800 lbf) at 17.1 mph.   **Wheel Dia:** 1143 mm.
Max. Speed: 90 mph.

D 5185-25035*§	Northampton Steam Railway	Darlington 1963
D 5207-25057*§	North Norfolk Railway	Derby 1963
D 5209*-25059§	Keighley and Worth Valley Railway	Derby 1963
D 5217*-25067§	Watercress Line	Derby 1963
D 5222*-25072§	Swindon & Crickade Railway	Derby 1963
D 5233-25083*	Crewe Heritage Centre	Derby 1963
D 7523-25173* "John F. Kennedy"	Crewe Heritage Centre	Derby 1965
D 7535*-25185 "MERCURY"	Paignton & Dartmouth Railway	Derby 1965
D 7541-25191*	North Yorkshire Moors Railway	Derby 1965
D 7585-25235*	Bo'ness & Kinneil Railway	Darlington 1964
D 7594-25244*	Swanage Railway	Darlington 1964
D 7612-25262*-25901	East Lancashire Railway	Derby 1966
D 7615-25265*	Peak Railway, Darley Dale	Derby 1965
D 7628*-25278	North Yorkshire Moors Railway	BP 8038/1965
D 7629*-25279	Llangollen Railway	BP 8039/1965
D 7633*-25283-25904	Severn Valley Railway	BP 8043/1965
D 7659-25309-25909*	East Lancashire Railway	BP 8069/1966
D 7663-25313*	Llangollen Railway	Derby 1966
D 7671*-25321	Midland Railway Centre	Derby 1967
D 7672*-25322-25912		Derby 1967

CLASS 27   Bo–Bo

Built: 1961–62 by the Birmingham Railway Carriage & Wagon Co. 69 built.
Engine: Sulzer 6LDA28B of 930 kW (1250 hp) at 750 rpm.
Transmission: Electric. Four GEC WT459 axle-hung traction motors.
Power at Rail: 696 kW (933 hp).
Max. T.E.: 178 kN (40000 lbf).   **Weight:** 75 tonnes.
Cont. T.E.: 111 kN (25000 lbf) at 14 mph.   **Wheel Dia:** 1092 mm.
Max. Speed: 90 mph.

D 5347-27001*	Caledonian Railway	BRCW DEL/190/1961
D 5351*-27005	Bo'ness & Kinneil Railway	BRCW DEL/194/1961
D 5353*-27007	Watercress Line	BRCW DEL/196/1961
D 5370-27024-ADB 968028*	Northampton Steam Railway	BRCW DEL/213/1962
D 5386*-27103-27212-27066	North Norfolk Railway	BRCW DEL/229/1962
D 5394*-27106-27050	Strathspey Railway	BRCW DEL/237/1962
D 5401*-27112-27056	Northampton Steam Railway	BRCW DEL/244/1962
D 5410*-27123-27205-27059	Birmingham Railway Museum	BRCW DEL/253/1962

CLASS 31 A1A–A1A

Built: 1957–62 by Brush Traction. 263 built.
Engine: English Electric 12SVT of 1100 kW (1470 hp) at 850 rpm.
Transmission: Electric. Four Brush TM73-68 axle-hung traction motors.
Power at Rail: kW (hp).
Max. T.E.: 190 kN (42800 lbf). **Weight:** 110 tonnes.
Cont. T.E.: 99 kN (22250 lbf) at 19.7 mph. **Wheel Dia:** 1092 mm.
Max. Speed: 80 mph.

D 5500*-31018 Steamtown, Carnforth (N) BE 71/1957

CLASS 28 METROVICK Co–Bo

Built: 1958–59 by Metropolitan Vickers. 20 built.
Engine: Crossley HSTVee 8 of 896 kW (1200 hp) at 625 rpm.
Transmission: Electric. Five MV 137BZ axle-hung traction motors.
Power at Rail: 671 kW (900 hp).
Max. T.E.: 223 kN (50000 lbf). **Weight:** 99 tonnes.
Cont. T.E.: 111 kN (25000 lbf) at 13.5 mph. **Wheel Dia:** 1003 mm.
Max. Speed: 75 mph.

D 5705*-S 15705-TDB 968006 Peak Railway, Matlock MV 1958

CLASS 33 Bo–Bo

Built: 1961–62 by the Birmingham Railway Carriage & Wagon Co. 98 built.
Engine: Sulzer 8LDA28 of 1160 kW (1550 hp) at 750 rpm.
Transmission: Electric. Four Crompton-Parkinson C171C2 axle-hung traction motors.
Power at Rail: 906 kW (1215 hp).
Max. T.E.: 200 kN (45000 lbf). **Weight:** 78 tonnes.
Cont. T.E.: 116 kN (26000 lbf) at 17.5 mph. **Wheel Dia:** 1092 mm.
Max. Speed: 85 mph.

D 6552-33034 MoDAD, Ludgershall, Wilts. BRCW DEL/144/1961

CLASS 35 HYMEK B–B

Built: 1961–64. Beyer Peacock. 101 built.
Engine: Maybach MD 870 of 1269 kW (1700 hp) at 1500 rpm.
Transmission: Hydraulic. Mekydro K184U.
Max. T.E.: 207 kN (46600 lbf). **Weight:** 77 tonnes.
Cont. T.E.: 151 kN (33950 lbf) at 12.5 mph. **Wheel Dia:** 1143 mm.
Max. Speed: 90 mph.

D 7017	West Somerset Railway	BP 7911/1962
D 7018	West Somerset Railway	BP 7912/1962
D 7029	North Yorkshire Moors Railway	BP 7923/1962
D 7076	East Lancashire Railway	BP 7980/1963

CLASS 20 Bo–Bo

Built: 1957–68 by English Electric. 228 built.
Engine: English Electric 8SVT of 746 kW (1000 hp) at 850 rpm.
Transmission: Electric. Four EE 526/5D axle-hung traction motors.
Power at Rail: 574 kW (770 hp).
Max. T.E.: 187 kN (42000 lbf). **Weight:** 74 tonnes.
Cont. T.E.: 111 kN (25000 lbf) at 11 mph. **Wheel Dia:** 1092 mm.
Max. Speed: 75 mph.

D 8000*-20050	National Railway Museum	EE/VF 2347/D375 1957
D 8031-20031*		EE/RSH 2753/8063 1960
D 8048-20048*		EE/VF 2770/D495 1959
D 8110-20110*		EE/RSH 3016/8268 1962
D 8327-20227*		EE/VF 3685/D1080 1968

CLASS 15 Bo–Bo

Built: 1957–59 by BTH/Clayton. 44 built.
Engine: Paxman 16YHXL of 597 kW (800 hp) at rpm.
Transmission: Electric. Four BTH 137AZ axle-hung traction motors.
Max. T.E.: 178 kN (40000 lbf). **Weight:** 69 tonnes.

Cont. T.E.: 88 kN (19700 lbf) at 11.3 mph.   **Wheel Dia**: 1003 mm.
Max. Speed: 60 mph.

D 8233*-ADB968001   Mangapps Farm, Burnham-on-Crouch   BTH 1131/1959

CLASS 17   Bo–Bo

Built: 1962–65. Clayton Equipment Co. 117 built.
Engine: Two Paxman 67HXL of 336 kW (450 hp) at 1500 rpm.
Transmission: Electric. Four GEC WT421 axle-hung traction motors.
Power at Rail: 461 kW (618 hp).
Max. T.E.: 178 kN (40000 lbf).   **Weight**: 69 tonnes.
Cont. T.E.: 80 kN (18000 lbf) at 12.8 mph.   **Wheel Dia**: 1003 mm.
Max. Speed: 60 mph.

D 8568   North Yorkshire Moors Railway   CE 4365U/69 1963

CLASS 55   DELTIC   Co–Co

Built: 1961–62. English Electric. 22 built.
Engine: Two Napier Deltic T18-25 of 1230 kW (1650 hp) at 1500 rpm.
Transmission: Electric. Six EE 538 axle-hung traction motors.
Power at Rail: 1969 kW (2640 hp).
Max. T.E.: 222 kN (50000 lbf).   **Weight**: 105 tonnes.
Cont. T.E.: 136 kN (30500 lbf) at 32.5 mph.   **Wheel Dia**: 1092 mm.
Max. Speed: 100 mph.

D 9000*-55022 ROYAL SCOTS GREY	BR Old Oak Common CARMD	EE/VF 2905/D557 1961
D 9002-55002* THE KINGS OWN YORKSHIRE LIGHT INFANTRY	National Railway Museum	EE/VF 2907/D559 1961
D 9009-55009* ALYCIDON	North Yorkshire Moors Rly.	EE/VF 2914/D556 1961
D 9015-55015* TULYAR	Midland Railway Centre	EE/VF 2920/D572 1961
D 9016*-55016 GORDON HIGHLANDER	BR Old Oak Common CARMD	EE/VF 2921/D573 1961
D 9019-55019-9019* ROYAL HIGHLAND FUSILIER		
	Great Central Railway	EE/VF 2924/D576 1961

D 9009 is under repair at ICI Wilton.

CLASS 14   0–6–0

Built: 1964–65 at Swindon. 56 built.
Engine: Paxman Ventura 6YJXL of 485 kW (650 hp) at 1500 rpm. (Rolls Royce†).
Transmission: Hydraulic. Voith L217u
Power at Rail: kW (hp).
Max. T.E.: 135 kN (30910 lbf).   **Weight**: 51 tonnes.
Cont. T.E.: 109 kN (26690 lbf) at 5.6 mph.   **Wheel Dia**: 1219 mm.
Max. Speed: 40 mph.

BR	Present		
D 9500	9312/92	West Somerset Railway	Swindon 1964
D 9502	9312/97	Llangollen Railway	Swindon 1964
D 9504	507	Kent & East Sussex Railway	Swindon 1964
D 9513	N.C.B. 38	Embsay Steam Railway	Swindon 1964
D 9515		Madrid Spain	Swindon 1964
D 9516		Nene Valley Railway	Swindon 1964
D 9518	No. 7 9312/95	Rutland Railway Museum	Swindon 1964
D 9520	45	Rutland Railway Museum	Swindon 1964
D 9521	9312/90 No. 3	Rutland Railway Museum	Swindon 1964
D 9523		Nene Valley Railway	Swindon 1964
D 9524	†	Bo'ness & Kinneil Railway	Swindon 1964
D 9525	49	Kent & East Sussex Railway	Swindon 1964
D 9526		West Somerset Railway	Swindon 1965
D 9529	14029	Nene Valley Railway	Swindon 1965
D 9531		East Lancashire Railway	Swindon 1965
D 9537		Gloucestershire–Warwickshire Railway	Swindon 1965
D 9539		Gloucestershire–Warwickshire Railway	Swindon 1965
D 9548	?	Madrid Spain	Swindon 1965
D 9549	?	Madrid Spain	Swindon 1965
D 9551		West Somerset Railway	Swindon 1965
D 9553		Gloucestershire–Warwickshire Railway	Swindon 1965
D 9555		Rutland Railway Museum	Swindon 1965

CLASS 97/6   0–6–0

Built: 1959 by Ruston & Hornsby at Lincoln.
Engine: Ruston 6VPH of 123 kW (165 hp).
Transmission: Electric. One British Thomson Houston RTA5041 traction motor.
Max. T.E.: 75 kN (17000 lbf).   **Weight:** 31 t.
Max. Speed: 20 mph.   **Wheel Dia.:** 978 mm.
RA: 1.
PWM 650-97650   Lincoln Holmes Yard   RSH 431757/1959

CLASS 98/1   0–6–0

Built: 1987 by Brecon Mountain railway. 1 built.
Engine: Caterpillar 3304T of 105 kW (140 hp).
Transmission: Hydraulic. Twin Disc torque converter.
Gauge: 1' 11½" **Weight:** 12.75 tonnes.
Max. Speed: 15 mph.   **Wheel Dia:** 610 mm.
10   Vale of Rheidol Railway   Brecon Mountain Rly 1987

EXPERIMENTAL DIESEL LOCOMOTIVES

PROTOTYPE DELTIC   Co–Co

Built: 1955. English Electric.
Engine: Two Napier Deltic T18-25 of 1230 kW (1650 hp) at 1500 rpm.
Transmission: Electric. Six EE 526A axle-hung traction motors.
Power at Rail: 1976 kW (2650 hp).
Max. T.E.: 267 kN (60000 lbf).   **Weight:** 107.7 tonnes.
Cont. T.E.: 104 kN (23400 lbf) at 43.5 mph. **Wheel Dia:** 1092 mm.
Max. Speed: 105 mph.
DELTIC   Science Museum, London (N)   EE 2007/1955

PROTOTYPE EE DE SHUNTER   0–6–0

Built: 1957. English Electric
Engine: English Electric 6RKT of 373 kW (500 hp) at 750 rpm.
Transmission: Electric.
Max. T.E.: 147 kN (33000 lbf).   **Weight:** 48 tonnes.
Cont. T.E.:   (lbf) at   mph.   **Wheel Dia:** 1219 mm.
Max. Speed: 35 mph.
D 226–D 0226*   Keighley & Worth Valley Railway   EE/VF 2345/D226 1956

NBL PROTOTYPE DH   0–4–0

Built: 1954.
Engine: Paxman 6 VRPHXL of 233 kW (312 hp) at 1250 rpm.
Transmission: Hydraulic. Voith L24V.
Max. T.E.: 112 kN (22850 lbf).   **Weight:** tonnes.
Wheel Dia: 1016 mm.   **Max. Speed:** 12 mph.

BR	Present		
	TOM	Telford Steam Railway	NBL 27414/1954
	TIGER	Isle of Wight Steam Railway	NBL 27415/1954

DEPARTMENTAL DIESEL LOCOMOTIVES

UNCLASSIFIED   0–4–0

Built: 1958. Ruston & Hornsby (36" gauge – being regauged to 1000 mm).
Engine: Ruston 4YC of 36 kW (48 hp) at 1375 rpm.
Transmission: Mechanical. Chain drive.
Max. T.E.: 18.7 kN (4200 lbf).   **Weight:**   tonnes.
Wheel Dia: 762 mm.
ED 10   Irchester Country Park   RH 411322/1958

UNCLASSIFIED
0–4–0

Built: 1957 Ruston & Hornsby (18″ gauge) for Horwich Works system. Now regauged to 600 mm.
Engine: Ruston 2VSH of 15 kW (20 hp) at 1200 rpm.
Transmission: Mechanical. Ruston 2 speed.
Max. T.E.: 8.4 kN (1890 lbf).
Weight: 3.56 tonnes.
Wheel Dia: 420 mm.

BR	Present		
ZM 32	416214	Gloddfa Ganol Centre	RH 416214/1957

UNCLASSIFIED
0–4–0

Built: 1956–1957 Ruston & Hornsby (24″ gauge) for Chesterton Junction Central Materials Depot, Cambridge.
Engine: Ruston.
Transmission: Mechanical.

BR	Present		
85049	Unnumbered	Northamptonshire Ironstone Railway	RH 393325/1956
85051		Cadeby Railway, Leicestershire	RH 404967/1957

ELECTRIC LOCOMOTIVES
CLASS 84
Bo–Bo

Built: 1960–61. North British Locomotive Co. 10 built. **System:** 25 kV ac overhead.
Continuous Rating: 2312 kW (3100 hp).
Max. T.E.: 222 kN (50000 lbf).
Weight: 76.6 tonnes.
Cont. T.E.: 78 kN (17600 lbf) at 66 mph.
Wheel Dia: 1219 mm.
Max. Speed: 100 mph.

E 3036-84001*	National Railway Museum	NBL 27793/1960

CLASS 71
Bo–Bo

Built: 1958–60. Doncaster. 24 built. **System:** 660–750 V dc third rail or overhead.
Continuous Rating: 1715 kW (2300 hp).
Max. T.E.: 191 kN (43 000 lbf).
Weight: 76.2 tonnes.
Cont. T.E.: 55 kN (12 400 lbf) at 69.6 mph.
Wheel Dia: 1219 mm.
Max. Speed: 90 mph.

E 5001*-71001	National Railway Museum	Doncaster 1959

GAS TURBINE VEHICLES
LOCOMOTIVE
AIA–AIA

Built: 1950. Brown Boveri
Power Unit: Brown Boveri gas turbine of 1828 kW (2450 hp).
Transmission: Electric. Four traction motors.
Max. T.E.: 140 kN (31500 lbf).
Weight: 117.1 tonnes.
Cont. T.E.: 55 kN (12400 lbf) at 64 mph.
Wheel Dias: 1232 mm.
Max. Speed: 90 mph.

18000	Vienna Arsenal Testing Station	BBC 4559/1950

EXPERIMENTAL ADVANCED PASSENGER TRAIN (APT-E)

Built: 1972 at Derby Litchurch Lane Works.
Power Units: Eight Leyland 350 automotive gas turbines of 222 kW (298 hp).
Traction Motors: Four GEC 253AY.

PC1	National Railway Museum	Derby 1972
PC2	National Railway Museum	Derby 1972
TC1	National Railway Museum	Derby 1972
TC2	National Railway Museum	Derby 1972

DIESEL MULTIPLE UNITS
CLASS 100
GLOUCESTER TWIN UNITS

Built: 1957–58. Normal formation: DMBS–DTCL.
Engines: Two AEC 220 of 112 kW (150 hp).

Transmission: Mechanical.
Max. Speed: 70 mph.

DMBS	17.53 x 2.82 m	30.5 tonnes	52S
DTCL	17.53 x 2.82 m	25.5 tonnes	12F 54S

SC	50341	DMBS	West Somerset Railway	Gloucester 1957
E	51118	DMBS	West Somerset Railway	Gloucester 1957
SC	56097	DTCL	West Somerset Railway	Gloucester 1957
M	56099	DTCL	West Somerset Railway	Gloucester 1957
E	56301	DTCL	Chasewater Light Railway	Gloucester 1957
E	56317	DTCL	Gwili Railway	Gloucester 1958

CLASS 103 — PARK ROYAL TWIN UNITS

Built: 1957–58. Normal formation: DMBS–DTCL.
Engines: Two AEC 220 of 112 kW (150 hp).
Transmission: Mechanical.
Max. Speed: 70 mph.

DMBS	17.53 x 2.82 m	34 tonnes	52S
DTCL	17.53 x 2.82 m	27 tonnes	16F 48S

M	50397	DMBS	Battlefield Steam Railway	PR 1957
W	50413	DMBS	West Somerset Railway	PR 1957
W	50414	DMBS	West Somerset Railway	PR 1957
M	56160§	DTCL	Battlefield Steam Railway	PR 1957
W	56168	DTCL	West Somerset Railway	PR 1957
W	56169	DTCL	West Somerset Railway	PR 1957

§ Also carried DB 975228.

CLASS 105 — CRAVEN TWIN UNIT

Built: 1956–59. Normal formation: DMBS–DTCL or DMCL.
Engines: Two AEC 220 of 112 kW (150 hp).
Transmission: Mechanical.
Max. Speed: 70 mph.

DMBS	17.53 x 2.82 m	29.5 tonnes	52S
DTCL	17.53 x 2.82 m	23.5 tonnes	12F 51S

E	51485	DMBS	West Somerset Railway	Cravens 1959
E	56121	DTCL	West Somerset Railway	Cravens 1959
E	56456-54456*	DTCL	Llangollen Railway	Cravens 1959

CLASS 108 — DERBY LIGHTWEIGHT

Built: 1958. Various formations.
Engines: Two Leyland of 112 kW (150 hp).
Transmission: Mechanical.
Max. Speed: 70 mph.

DMBS	18.49 x 2.82 m	29.5 tonnes	52S
DMCL	18.49 x 2.82 m	28.5 tonnes	12F 53S
DTCL	18.49 x 2.82 m	21.5 tonnes	12F 53S
TBSL	18.49 x 2.82 m	21.5 tonnes	50S

M	51941	DMBS	Severn Valley Railway	Derby 1961
M	52064	DMCL	Severn Valley Railway	Derby 1961
M	56207*–54207	DTCL	British Steel, Scunthorpe	Derby 1958
M	59245	TBSL	British Steel, Scunthorpe	Derby 1958

CLASS 109 — WICKHAM TWIN UNITS

Built: 1958. Normal formation: DMBS–DTCL.
Engines: Two BUT (Leyland) of 112 kW (150 hp).
Transmission: Mechanical.
Max. Speed: 70 mph.

DMBS	17.53 x 2.82 m	27.5 tonnes	52S
DTCL	17.53 x 2.82 m	20.5 tonnes	16F 50S

E	50415	DMBS	Trinidad Government	Wickham 1957
E	50416-DB 975005	DMBS	Chasewater Light Railway	Wickham 1957
E	50418	DMBS	Trinidad Government	Wickham 1957
E	56170	DTCL	Trinidad Government	Wickham 1957
E	56171-DB 975006	DTCL	Chasewater Light Railway	Wickham 1957
E	56174	DTCL	Trinidad Government	Wickham 1957

CLASS 110   BRCW CALDER VALLEY UNITS

Built: 1961–2. Normal formation: DMBC–TSL–DMCL.
Engines: Two Rolls-Royce C6NFLH38D of 134 kW (180 hp).
Transmission: Mechanical.
Max. Speed: 70 mph.

DMBC	17.53 x 2.82 m	32.5 tonnes	12F 33S	
DMCL	17.53 x 2.82 m	32.5 tonnes	12F 54S	
E	51813	DMBC	East Lancashire Railway	BRCW 1961
E	51842	DMCL	East Lancashire Railway	BRCW 1961
E	52071	DMBC	Lakeside & Haverthwaite Railway	BRCW 1962
E	52077	DMCL	Lakeside & Haverthwaite Railway	BRCW 1961

CLASS 111   METRO CAMMELL TRAILER BUFFET

Built: 1960. Formerly part of a four car unit.
Max. Speed: 70 mph.

TSLRB	17.53 x 2.82 m	25.5 tonnes	53S	
E	59575	TSLRB	Greater Manchester Mus. of Sc. & T.	Metro-Cammell 1960

CLASS 116   DERBY SUBURBAN TRAILERS

Built: 1957–58. Non-gangwayed.
Max. Speed: 70 mph.

TS	19.42 x 2.82 m	29 tonnes	100S	
TC	19.42 x 2.82 m	29 tonnes	20F 68S	
M	59003	TS	Paignton & Dartmouth Railway	Derby 1957
M	59004	TS	Paignton & Dartmouth Railway	Derby 1957
M	59444	TC	Chasewater Light Railway	Derby 1957

CLASS 120   SWINDON CROSS-COUNTRY TRAILER BUFFET

Built: 1957–61. Normal formation: DMBC–TSLRB–DMSL.
Max. Speed: 70 mph.

TSLRB	19.66 x 2.82 m	31.5 tonnes	60S	
M	59276	TSLRB	Great Central Railway	Swindon 1958

CLASS 126   SWINDON INTER-CITY 3-CAR UNITS

Built: 1959. Normal formation: DMBSL TSK DMSL.
Engines: Two AEC 220 of 112 kW (150 hp).
Transmission: Mechanical.
Max. Speed: 70 mph.

DMBSL	19.66 x 2.82 m	38.5 tonnes	52S	
TSK	19.66 x 2.82 m	32.3 tonnes	56S	
DMSL	19.66 x 2.82 m	38.5 tonnes	64S	
TFLRB	19.66 x 2.82 m	34 tonnes	18F 12S	

§ Used as hauled stock.
† Used as camping coaches.

SC 51017	DMSL	Caledonian Railway	Swindon 1959
SC 51043	DMBSL	Caledonian Railway	Swindon 1959
SC 59098†	TFLRB	North Yorkshire Moors Railway	Swindon 1961
SC 59099†	TFLRB	North Yorkshire Moors Railway	Swindon 1961
SC 59404	TSK	Caledonian Railway	Swindon 1959
SC 79091	DM	Lamco Mining Co., Liberia	Swindon 1956
SC 79093	DM	Lamco Mining Co., Liberia	Swindon 1956
SC 79094	DM	Lamco Mining Co., Liberia	Swindon 1956
SC 79096	DM	Lamco Mining Co., Liberia	Swindon 1956
SC 79097	DM	Lamco Mining Co., Liberia	Swindon 1956
SC 79441§	TFLRB	Strathspey Railway	Swindon 1956
SC 79443†	TFLRB	North Yorkshire Moors Railway	Swindon 1956

CLASS 127   DERBY SUBURBAN POWER CARS

Built: 1959. Normal formation: DMBS–TSL–TS–DMBS.
Engines: Two Rolls-Royce C8 of 177 kW (238 hp).
Transmission: Hydraulic.   **Max. Speed:** 70 mph.
DMBS   19.51 x 2.82 m   40.6 tonnes   76S
DMPMV (A)   19.51 x 2.82 m   40 tonnes
DMPMV (B)   19.51 x 2.82 m   40 tonnes

M	51592	DMBS	Paignton & Dartmouth Railway	Derby 1959
M	51604	DMBS	Paignton & Dartmouth Railway	Derby 1959
M	51616	DMBS	Great Central Railway	Derby 1959
M	51618	DMBS	Llangollen Railway	Derby 1959
M	51622	DMBS	Great Central Railway	Derby 1959
55966*–M	51591	DMPMV(A)	Midland Railway Centre	Derby 1959
55967*–M	51610	DMPMV(B)	Swindon & Cricklade Railway	Derby 1959
55976*–M	51625	DMPMV(A)	Midland Railway Centre	Derby 1959

CLASS 201   HASTINGS LINE 6-CAR DIESEL-ELECTRIC UNITS

Built: 1957 by BR Eastleigh Works on frames constructed at Ashford. Special narrow-bodied units built to the former loading gauge of the Hastings line. Normal formation: DMSO–TSOL–TSOL–TFK–TSOL–DMS.
Engines: English Electric 4SRKT of 370 kW (500 hp).
Transmission: Two EE 507 traction motors on the inner power car bogie.
Max. Speed: 75 mph.
DMSO   17.68 x 2.50 m   54 tonnes   22S
TSOL   17.68 x 2.50 m   29 tonnes   52S
TFK   17.68 x 2.50 m   30 tonnes   42F

S	60000	DMSO	St. Leonards Railway Engineering	Ashford/Eastleigh 1957
S	60001	DMSO	St. Leonards Railway Engineering	Ashford/Eastleigh 1957
S	60500	TSOL	St. Leonards Railway Engineering	Ashford/Eastleigh 1957
S	60501	TSOL	St. Leonards Railway Engineering	Ashford/Eastleigh 1957
S	60502	TSOL	St. Leonards Railway Engineering	Ashford/Eastleigh 1957
S	60700	TFK	St. Leonards Railway Engineering	Ashford/Eastleigh 1957

CLASS 202   HASTINGS LINE 6-CAR DIESEL-ELECTRIC UNITS

Built: 1957–58 by BR Eastleigh Works on frames constructed at Ashford. Special narrow-bodied units built to the former loading gauge of the Hastings line. Normal formation: DMSO–TSOL–TSOL (or TRB)–TFK–TSOL–DMS.
Engines: English Electric 4SRKT of 370 kW (500 hp).
Transmission: Two EE 507 traction motors on the inner power car bogie.
Max. Speed: 75 mph.
DMSO   19.66 x 2.50 m   55 tonnes   30S
TSOL   19.66 x 2.50 m   29 tonnes   60S
TFK   19.66 x 2.50 m   31 tonnes   48F
TRB   19.66 x 2.50 m   3? tonnes

S	60016	DMSO	Swanage Railway	Ashford/Eastleigh 1957
S	60018	DMSO	Swanage Railway	Ashford/Eastleigh 1957
S	60019	DMSO	St. Leonards Railway Engineering	Ashford/Eastleigh 1957
S	60527	TSOL	Swanage Railway	Ashford/Eastleigh 1957
S	60528	TSOL	St. Leonards Railway Engineering	Ashford/Eastleigh 1957
S	60529	TSOL	St. Leonards Railway Engineering	Ashford/Eastleigh 1957
S	60708	TFK	St. Leonards Railway Engineering	Ashford/Eastleigh 1957
S	60709	TFK	St. Leonards Railway Engineering	Ashford/Eastleigh 1957
S	60750	TRB	St. Leonards Railway Engineering	Ashford/Eastleigh 1958

DIESEL RAILBUSES

UNCLASSIFIED   WAGGON UND MASCHINENBAU

Built: 1958. 5 built.
Engine: Buessing of 112 kW (150 hp) at 1900 rpm. († AEC 220 of 112kW (150hp))
Transmission: Mechanical.   **Max. Speed:** 70 mph.
DMS   12.87 x 2.67 m   15 tonnes   56S

BR	Present		
E	79960	North Norfolk Railway	WMD 1265/1958
E	79962	Keighley & Worth Valley Railway	WMD 1267/1958
E	79963	North Norfolk Railway	WMD 1268/1958
E	79964† M 79964	Keighley & Worth Valley Railway	WMD 1298/1958

UNCLASSIFIED — AC CARS

Built: 1958.
Engine: AEC 220 of 112 kW (150 hp). (§ engine removed)
Transmission: Mechanical.
Max. Speed: 70 mph.
DMS   11.08 x 2.74 m   11 tonnes   46S

| W | 79976§ | Bodmin Steam Railway | AC 1958 |
| W | 79978 | Colne Valley Railway | AC 1958 |

UNCLASSIFIED — BR DERBY/LEYLAND

Built: 1980.
Engine: Leyland TL11.
Transmission: Mechanical. Self Changing Gears.
Max. Speed: 75 mph.
DMS   12.32 x 2.50 m   16.67 tonnes   40S

| RDB 975874 | National Railway Museum | RTC Derby 1980 |

UNCLASSIFIED — BREL DERBY/LEYLAND

Built: 1981.
Engine: Leyland 690 of 149 kW (200 hp).
Transmission: Mechanical. Self Changing Gears SE4 epicyclic gearbox and cardan shafts to SCG RF28 final drive.
Max. Speed: 75 mph.
DMS   15.30 x 2.50 m   19.96 tonnes   56S

| R3*–RDB 977020 | Northern Ireland Railways | RTC Derby 1980 |

▼Former 'Brighton Belle' DMPBS Car No. 91 stands at Sheringham on the North Norfolk railway looking a little scruffy on 1st August 1990.   *Chris Wilson*

BATTERY ELECTRIC MULTIPLE UNIT
UNCLASSIFIED   BR DERBY/COWLAIRS

Built: 1958.
Power: 216 lead-acid cells of 1070 Ah.
Traction Motors: Two 100 kW Siemens nose-suspended motors. **Max. Speed:** 70 mph.

DMBS	17.52 x 2.79 m	37.5 tonnes	52S
DTCL	17.52 x 2.79 m	32.5 tonnes	12F 53S

SC 79998-DB 975003*	DMBS	East Lancashire Railway		1958
SC 79999-DB 975004*	DTCL	East Lancashire Railway		1958

ELECTRIC MULTIPLE UNITS
CLASS 501   BR ASHFORD/EASTLEIGH

Built: 1957. **Normal Formation:** DBSO–TSO–DTBSO. **System:** 630 V dc third rail.
Max. Speed: 60 mph.

TSO	17.42 x 2.82 m	29.5 tonnes	92S
DTBSO	17.52 x 2.82 m	30.5 tonnes	74S

BR	*Present*		
M 70170	TSO	Marchwood Military Railway	Ash/Elh 1957
M 75186	DTBSO	Marchwood Military Railway	Ash/Elh 1957

CLASS 370
PROTOTYPE ADVANCED PASSENGER TRAIN (APT-P)

Built: 197 –8 . Designed to run as pairs of six-car articulated units with two power cars in the middle, these electric trains featured active hydraulic tilt and proved to be a maintenance nightmare. The power cars were reasonably successful, and are partly the basis of the class 91 locomotive.
System: 25 kV ac overhead.
Normal Formation of Trailer Rake: DTS–TS–TSRB–TU–TF–TBF.
Formation: DTSO–TBFO–2M–TRSB–TBFO–DTSO.
Traction Motors.: Four ASEA LJMA 410F body mounted.
Wheel Dia: 853 mm.
Max. Speed: 125 mph.

DTSO	33.7 tonnes	52S
TBFO	31.9 tonnes	25F
TRSB	26.75 tonnes	28S
M	67.5 tonnes	

SC 48103	DTSO	Crewe Heritage Centre	Derby LL 198
SC 48106	DTSO	Crewe Heritage Centre	Derby LL 198
SC 48602	TBFO	Crewe Heritage Centre	Derby LL 198
SC 48603	TBFO	Crewe Heritage Centre	Derby LL 198
SC 48404	TRSB	Crewe Heritage Centre	Derby LL 198
SC 49002	M	Crewe Heritage Centre	Derby LL 198
SC 49006	M	Crewe Heritage Centre	Derby LL 198

PROTOTYPE HIGH SPEED TRAIN POWER CAR
CLASS 252   HST POWER CAR

Built: 1972.
Engine: Paxman Valenta 12RP200L of 1680 kW (2250 hp) at 1500 rpm.
Traction Motors: Four Brush TMH 68-46.
Power at Rail: 1320 kW (1770 hp).
Max. T.E.: 80 kN (17 980 lbf).   **Weight:** 67 tonnes.
Cont. T.E.: 46 kN (10 340 lbf) at 64.5 mph.   **Wheel Dia:** 1020 mm.
Max. Speed: 125 mph.

41001-W43000*-ADB975812	National Railway Museum (N)	Derby 1972

LIST OF LOCATIONS

The following is a list of UK locations where former BR locos can be found, together with Ordnance Survey grid references where these are known. Please note that industrial sites where preserved locos are kept are classed as preservation sites. Industrial locations are those where the locos are in industrial use.

PRESERVATION SITES & OPERATING RAILWAYS

§ denotes not normally open to the public.

	OS GRID REF.
Avon Valley Railway, Bitton Station, Bristol, Avon.	ST 670705
Battlefield Steam Railway, Shackerstone Station, Leicestershire.	SK 379066
A.J.R. Birch & Son Ltd., Hope Farm, Sellindge, Kent §.	TR 119388
Birmingham Museum of Science & Industry, Newhall St., Birmingham, West Midlands.	
	SP 064874
Birmingham Railway Museum, Tyseley Depot, Birmingham, West Midlands.	SP 105841
Bluebell Railway, Sheffield Park, East Sussex.	TQ 403238
Blue Circle Cement, Hamworthy Junction., Poole, Dorset §.	SS 988918
Bodmin Steam Railway, Bodmin General Station, Bodmin., Cornwall.	SX 073664
Bombardier Prorail, Horbury, Wakefield, West Yorkshire §.	SK 304176
Bo'ness & Kinneil Railway, Bo'ness, West Lothian.	NT 003817
BREL Ltd.,Crewe Works §	SJ 691561
Bressingham Gardens, Diss, Norfolk.	TM 080806
Brighton Locomotive Works, Preston Park, Brighton, West Sussex §.	TQ 302061
British Steel, Appleby-Frodingham Works, Scunthorpe, Humberside §.	SE 910110
BRML Eastleigh Works, Eastleigh, Hampshire §.	SU 457185
Buckinghamshire Railway Centre, Quainton Road Station, Aylesbury, Bucks.	SP 736189
Bulmers Railway Centre, Hereford, Hereford & Worcester.	SO 505402
Butetown Historic Railway Society Bute Street Docks, Cardiff., South Glamorgan	ST 192745
Cadeby Light Railway, Market Bosworth, Leicestershire.	SK 426024
Caerphilly Railway Soc., Harold Wilson Industrial Estate, Caerphilly, Mid Glamorgan §.	ST 113865
Caledonian Railway, Brechin Station, Montrose, Tayside.	NO 603603
Canterbury Heritage Centre, Stour Street, Canterbury, Kent.	TQ 146577
Cargo Fleet, Cleveland (exact location not known) §.	
Chasewater Light Railway, Chasewater Park, Brownhills, Staffordshire.	SK 034070
Chatterley Whitfield Mining Museum, Tunstall, Stoke-on-Trent, Staffs.	SJ 883531
Cholsey & Wallingford Railway, Wallingford, Oxfordshire.	SU 599891
CIL Storefitters, Finsbury Park, London.	TQ 313867
Colne Valley Railway, Castle Hedingham Station, Halstead, Essex.	TL 774362
Crewe Heritage Centre, Crewe, Cheshire	SJ 708552
Darlington North Road Station Railway. Museum, Darlington, Co. Durham.	NZ 289157
Darlington Railway Centre, Darlington, Co. Durham.	NZ 290156
Dean Forest Railway, Norchard, Gloucestershire.	SO 629044
Diamond House, Church Street, South Leverton, Nottinghamshire §.	SK 783810
Didcot Railway Centre (Great Western Society), Didcot, Oxfordshire.	SU 524906
East Anglian Railway Museum, Chappel & Wakes Colne Station, Essex.	TL 898289
East Lancashire Railway, Bolton Street, Bury, Greater Manchester.	SD 803109
East Somerset Railway, Cranmore, Somerset.	ST 664429
Embsay Steam Railway, Embsay Station, Embsay, North Yorkshire.	SE 007533
Fleetwood Locomotive Centre, Jameson Road, Fleetwood, Lancashire.	SD 335468
Glasgow Museum of Transport, 25 Albert Drive, Coplawhill, Glasgow, Strathclyde.	NS 581632
Gloddfa Ganol Mountain Tourist Centre, Blaenau Ffestiniog, Gwynedd.	SH 693470
Gloucestershire-Warwickshire Railway, Toddington Station, Gloucestershire.	SP 020323
Great Central Railway, Loughborough Central Station, Leicestershire.	SK 543194
Greater Manchester Museum of Science & Industry, Liverpool Road, Manchester.	SJ 831978
Great Western Railway Museum, Faringdon Road, Swindon, Wiltshire.	SU 145846
Gwili Railway, Bronwydd Arms Station, Carmarthen, Clywd.	SN 417236
Herring Brothers, Bicester Timber Yard, Bicester, Oxfordshire §.	SP
Humberside Locomotive Preservation Group, Dairycoates Depot, Hull, Humberside.	TA 068269
The Industrial Adventure, Snibston Mine, Coalville, Leicestershire	SK 420144
Irchester Narrow Gauge Railway, Irchester Country Park, Irchester, Beds.	SP 904659
Isle of Wight Steam Railway, Havenstreet Station, Isle of Wight.	SZ 556898
Keighley & Worth Valley Railway, Haworth, Keighley, West Yorkshire.	SE 034371
Kent & East Sussex Railway, Tenterden Station, Tenterden, Kent.	TQ 882336
Lakeside & Haverthwaite Railway, Haverthwaite, Cumbria.	SD 349843

Lavender Line, Isfield, East Sussex	TQ 452171
MoDAD, Central Vehicle Depot, Ludgershall, Wiltshire §.	SU 261507
Leeds City Museum of Industry & Science, Canal Road, Leeds.	SE 275342
Lincoln Holmes Yard	SK
Lincoln Station	SK 975709
Liverpool Museum, William Brown Street, Liverpool.	SJ 349908
Llangollen Railway, Llangollen Station, Clwyd.	SJ 211423
Long Marston Pattern Shop (ex MoD), Long Marston, Warwickshire §.	SP 152469
Lytham Motive Power Museum, Dock Road, Lytham, Lancashire.	SD 381276
W.H. McAlpine, Fawley Hill, Fawley Green, near Henley-on-Thames, Oxfordshire §.	SU 755861
Mangapp's Farm, Burnham-on-Crouch, Essex.	TQ 944980
Markinch Goods Depot, Markinch, Fife §.	NO 299013
Middleton Railway, Hunslet, Leeds, West Yorkshire.	SE 302309
Midland Railway Centre, Butterley Station, Ripley, Derbyshire.	SK 403520
Museum of Army Transport, Beverley, North Humberside	TA 041392
Narrow Gauge Railway Museum, Wharf Station, Tywyn, Gwynedd.	SH 586004
National Railway Museum, Leeman Road, York, North Yorkshire.	SE 594519
National Tramway Museum, Clay Cross, Derbyshire.	SK 402652
National Tramway Museum, Crich, Derbyshire.	SK 345549
Nene Valley Railway, Wansford Station, Peterborough, Cambridgeshire.	TL 093979
Northamptonshire Ironstone Railway, Hunsbury Hill, Northampton.	SP 735584
Northampton Steam Railway, Pitsford, Northamptonshire.	SP 736666
North Norfolk Railway, Sheringham Station, Norfolk.	TG 156430
North of England Open Air Museum, Beamish Hall, Beamish, Tyne & Wear.	NZ 217547
North Staffordshire Railway, Cheddleton Station, Staffordshire.	SJ 983519
North Tyneside Railway, Middle Engine Lane, North Tyneside, Tyne & Wear.	NZ 323693
North Woolwich Station Museum, North Woolwich, London.	TQ 433798
North Yorkshire Moors Railway, Grosmont Station, North Yorkshire.	NZ 828049
Paignton & Dartmouth Railway, Queen's Park Station, Paignton, Devon.	SX 889606
Peak Railway, Darley Dale Station, Derbyshire.	SK 273626
Peak Railway, Matlock Station, Derbyshire.	SK 296603
Plym Valley Railway, Marsh Mills, Plymouth, Devon.	SX 521566
Pontypool & Blaenavon Railway, Furnoe Sidings, Blaenavon.	SO 237093
"Poplars", North Moreton, Nr. Didcot, Oxfordshire §.	SU 552904
Richborough Power Station, Richborough, Kent §	TR 334620
Rowden Mill Station, near Bromyard, Hereford & Worcester	SO 627565
Royal Victoria Dock, London	
Rutland Railway Museum, Cottesmore, Leicestershire.	SK 887137
Sail & Steam Engineering, Brightlingsea, Essex §.	TM 689163
Science Museum, Imperial Institute Road, South Kensington, London.	TQ 268793
Scolton Manor Museum, Scolton Manor, Haverfordwest, Dyfed	SM 991222
Scottish Industrial Railway Centre, Minnivy Colliery, Dalmellington, Ayrshire	NS 476074
Severn Valley Railway, Bewdley Station, Hereford & Worcester.	SO 793753
Severn Valley Railway, Bridgnorth Station, Shropshire.	SO 715926
Southall Railway Centre, Southall, Greater London. §	TQ 131798
South Devon Railway, Buckfastleigh, Devon.	SX 747633
South Yorkshire Railway Museum, Meadowhall, Sheffield, South Yorkshire.	SK 383890
St. Leonards Railway Engineering, St. Leonards, East Sussex.	TQ 778086
Steamport Railway Museum, Derby Road, Southport, Merseyside.	SD 341170
Steamtown Railway Leisure Centre, Carnforth, Lancashire.	SD 496708
Strathspey Railway, Aviemore, Highland Region.	NH 898131
Swanage Railway, Swanage Station, Dorset.	SZ 028789
Swansea Vale Railway, Swansea, West Glamorgan.	SS 660928
Swindon & Cricklade Railway, Blunsdon Station Site, Swindon, Wiltshire.	SU 110897
Swindon Railway Engineering Ltd. (former Swindon Works), Swindon, Wiltshire.	SU 140846
Talyllyn Railway, Tywyn Pendre Depot, Tywyn, Gwynedd.	SH 590008
Telford Steam Railway, Horsehay, Telford, Shropshire.	SJ 675073
Tiverton Museum, Tiverton, Devon.	SS 954124
Vale of Neath Railway, Cadoxton Site, Neath, West Glamorgan	SS 761988
Vale of Rheidol Railway, Aberystwyth, Dyfed	SN 587812
Venice-Simplon Orient Express, Stewarts Lane , Battersea, London §.	TQ 257798
Victoria Park, Leamington Spa, Warwickshire.	SP 311655
Wanstrow Childrens Playground, Wanstrow, Somerset	ST 712417
Watercress Line, Alresford Station, Alresford, Hampshire.	SU 588325
Welshpool & Llanfair Railway, Llanfair Caereinon, Powyis.	SJ 107069
West Somerset Railway, Minehead Station, Somerset.	SS 975463
Wirral BC, Birkenhead Central Depot, Birkenhead, Merseyside	SJ 324884

INDUSTRIAL LOCATIONS

BCOE, Oxcroft DP, Clowne, Derbyshire.	SK 469741
Birds Commercial Metals, Long Marston, Worcestershire.	SP 154458
Booth-Roe Metals, Armer Street, Rotherham, South Yorkshire.	SK 421924
Bowaters (UK) Paper Co., Sittingbourne Works, Sittingbourne, Kent.	TQ 920667
BREL, Crewe Works, Crewe, Cheshire.	SJ 691561
BREL, Derby Carriage Works, Lichurch Lane, Derby, Derbyshire.	SK 364345
BREL, York Works, York, North Yorkshire.	SE 587516
British Cellophane, Bridgewater, Somerset.	ST 309382
British Fuels, Blackburn Coal Concentration Depot, Lancashire.	SD 677275
British Salt, Middlewich, Cheshire.	SJ 718645
British Sugar, Woodston, Peterborough.	TL 175976
Butterley Co. Ltd., Butterley Works, Ripley, Derbyshire.	SK 405518
Coal Mechanisation, Tolworth Coal Concentration Depot, London.	TQ 198656
Cobra Railfreight., North Road, Middlesbrough, Cleveland.	NZ 488209
Costain Dowmac, Lenwade, Norfolk.	TF 114179
A.V. Dawson, Depot Road, Middlesbrough, Cleveland.	NZ 493215
Day & Sons, Brentford Town Goods Depot, Brentford, London.	TQ 166778
Deanside Transit, Hillington, Glasgow, Strathclyde.	NS 526652
Dower Wood, Newmarket Grain Terminal, Newmarket, Suffolk.	TL 645628
Dow Chemicals, Kings Lynn, Norfolk.	TF 613215
English China Clay Ports, Blackpool Works, Methrose, Burngullow, Cornwall.	
English China Clay Ports, Fowey, Cornwall.	SX 125530
Felixstowe Dock & Railway Company, Felixstowe, Suffolk.	TM 283330
600 Ferrous Fragmentisers, Willesden, London.	TO 215829
Fire Service Training Centre, Moreton-in-Marsh, Gloucestershire.	
Ford Motor Company, Dagenham, London.	TQ 496825
Foster Yeoman, Merehead Stone Terminal, Shepton Mallet, Somerset.	ST 693426
Glaxochem, Plumpton Junction, Ulverston, Cumbria.	SD 306779
Arthur Guinness, Park Royal Brewery, Park Royal, London.	TQ 195828
Gulf Oil Company, Waterston, Milford Haven, Dyfed.	SM 935055
Hargreaves Ltd., British Oak DP, Crigglestone, West Yorkshire.	SE 300164
Humberside Sea & Land Services, Grimsby, Humberside.	
ICI Wilton Works, Middlesbrough, Cleveland.	NZ 564218
Independant Sea Terminals, Ridham Dock, Swale, Kent.	TQ 918684
Kemira Fertilisers, Ince Marshes, Ellesmere Port, Cheshire.	SJ 472765
LCP Fuels, Shut End, Brierley Hill, West Midlands.	SO 901897
Marchwood Military Railway, Marchwood, Hampshire.	SU 395103
Mayer-Parry Recycling Ltd., Snailwell, Newmarket, Cambridgeshire.	TL 638678
MoDAD, Long Marston, Warwickshire.	SP
NSF, Monkton Coking Plant, Hebburn, Tyne & Wear.	NZ 316627
Otis Euro Trans-Rail, Salford, Greater Manchester.	
GG Papworth, Queen Adelaide, Ely, Cambridgeshire.	TL 563810
PD Fuels, Coed Bach DP, Kidwelly, Dyfed.	SN 424059
PD Fuels, Gwaun-Cae-Gurwen DP, West Glamorgan.	SN 713120
Port of Boston Ltd., Boston Docks, Lincolnshire.	
Redland Aggregates, Barrow-on-Soar Works, Leicestershire.	SK 587168
RFS Industries, Doncaster Wagon Works, Doncaster, South Yorkshire.	SK 569031
RFS Industries, Kilnhurst, Rotherham, South Yorkshire.	SK 464973
Scottish Grain Distillers, Cambus, Alloa, Central Region.	NS 854940
Sheerness Steel Co., Sheerness, Kent.	TQ 912748
Tilcon, Swinden Limeworks, Grassington, North Yorkshire.	SE 605539
Trafford Park Estates, Trafford Park, Manchester, Greater Manchester.	ST 786971
Vic Berry, Western Boulevard, Leicester, Leicestershire.	SK 580035
Wiggins Teape, Corpach, Fort William, Highland Region.	NN 083776

PUBLIC HOUSES & HOTELS

Black Bull, Moulton, North Yorkshire.	NZ 237037
Brighton Belle, Winsford, Cheshire.	SJ 672661
Cardiff Holiday Inn, Cardiff, South Glamorgan.	ST 185759
Little Mill Inn, Rowarth, Mellor, Derbyshire.	SK 011890
Nags Head, Mickleover, Derbyshire.	SK 307342